Biomechanics
of
Human Motion

MARIAN WILLIAMS, Ph. D.
Late Associate Professor of Physical Ther-
apy, Department of Allied Medical Sciences,
and Assistant Professor, Department of
Anatomy, Stanford University School of
Medicine, Stanford

HERBERT R. LISSNER
Chairman of the Department and Professor
of Engineering Mechanics, and Coordinator
of Biomechanics Research Center, Wayne
State University, Detroit

W. B. SAUNDERS COMPANY
PHILADELPHIA · LONDON

W. B. Saunders Company: West Washington Square
Philadelphia, Pa.   19105

12 Dyott Street
London, WC1A   1DB

1835 Yonge Street
Toronto 7, Ontario

Biomechanics of Human Motion   SBN 0-7216-9440-3

Print No.:   6   7   8   9

Preface

THIS TEXT represents an integration of material from two fields. In it the principles of engineering mechanics are applied to the activities and fundamental knowledge of the physical therapist. While many of the examples have been selected from the clinical area, the analysis of muscle and joint function and of external forces acting on the body has a broad application far beyond the scope of any single professional group. It is of importance to all students of human motion in both its normal and pathological aspects.

The science of mechanics is so basic and familiar that its existence is often overlooked. Whenever we pick up an object, push open a door, walk or stand still, our bodies are under the constant influence of various forces. When the laws of mechanics are learned and applied in theory and practice, we achieve an understanding which is impossible without recognition of this subject. As early as the fifteenth century Leonardo da Vinci, one of the world's greatest artists and a scientist years ahead of his time, recognized the significance of mechanics in his biological studies. He wrote, "Mechanical science [or the science of mechanics] is the noblest and above all others the most useful, seeing that by means of it all animated bodies which have movement perform all their actions."

Since the days of da Vinci the science of mechanics has been developed and formalized so that in the usual study the subject is treated for itself and its wide applications are not fully explored. The student of physical therapy or physical education, to whom the subject of mechanics is usually presented as a division of physics, has difficulty in carrying over the full implications of his basic coursework into actual practice later on. We have attempted to bridge this gap by developing many illustrations throughout the text and by setting up and solving a variety of problems both in functional anatomy and treatment.

The main purpose of this text is to suggest techniques for approaching problems. Systems of forces are considered with increasing levels of complexity. In setting up problems, the characteristics of external forces can often be measured or accurately estimated. However, calculation of internal forces of muscles and joints at the present time requires some degree of simplification. As more information relative to segment mass, center of gravity locations and other anthropometric data becomes available, and as instrumentation in the study of kinesiology continues to improve, estimates of internal forces will become more accurate. In the present text, the principles of statics are utilized in the analysis of problems, with emphasis on the very useful device of the free body diagram. It is hoped that as persons dealing with human motion become versed in these techniques of analysis they will see many ramifications in their own particular fields of activity. Certainly many areas for research are suggested in the material presented.

The authors are grateful to the National Foundation for making publication of this book possible. We wish also to thank Mr. Maurice Gallott who was responsible for the illustrations, with assistance from Miss Jo Ann Crow.

M. W.
H. R. L.

Contents

Chapter 8
Friction **115**

Appendix A

Appendix B

Appendix C

CHAPTER ONE

Basic Considerations

Mechanics is the subject of forces and their effects. It relates the forces in muscles, bones, and joints with externally applied loads. Clinically such loads or forces may result from the pull of gravity on the body parts, or from resistance which is applied to the segment.

The clinical area provides many examples. Manual muscle testing depends on the skill of the physical therapist in applying test forces of varying degrees of magnitude in order to gauge the patient's ability to resist these forces. External forces are also applied in the stretching of muscle contractures by the therapist. The patient may wear a brace or corset, may support himself on crutches or a cane, or may help himself up or down stairs by gripping the stair rail. Still another example of externally applied forces is the use of skeletal traction systems for patients who have broken an arm or a leg or who have spinal disabilities. The "internal" forces applied to the skeleton by contracting muscles are also analyzed according to the laws of mechanics.

Gravity produces a constant external force the effect of which is sometimes neutralized, for therapeutic purposes, by immersion of the body or a segment of the body in a tank of water (Fig. 1.1). In this case the gravitational force is

1

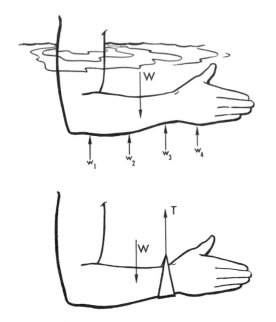

Fig. 1.1.   Here the forearm weight (W) is supported by the buoyancy of the water (w). Recall that the weight of the water displaced is equal to the weight of the forearm. A sling at the wrist pulling upward with force T can also be used to oppose W.

balanced by the force of buoyancy since the body is buoyed up by a force equal to the weight of the volume of water it displaces. Another method of accomplishing this "weightlessness" is by suspension in slings as advocated by Guthrie-Smith.[1]

The practicing therapist may not need exact computations of many of the forces with which he works. He recognizes the importance of such factors as lever action, the concept of the center of gravity of the body and its component parts, and their relation to the base of support and to stance and locomotion. However, the therapist will function most effectively and find his job most interesting when he has a clear understanding of the principles of mechanics as they apply to his work. This, then, is our goal in the present text.

The whole subject of mechanics covers two basic areas:

1. *Statics,* the study of bodies remaining at rest or in equilibrium as a result of forces acting upon them.

2. *Dynamics,* the study of moving bodies. Dynamics, in turn, may be subdivided into *kinematics* and *kinetics.*

Kinematics might be called the science of

motion, since it deals with the relationships that exist between displacements, velocities, and accelerations in all kinds of motion. It does not concern itself with the forces involved but only with a description of the movements themselves. *Kinetics* deals with moving bodies and the forces that act to produce the motion. As an example, Eberhart et al.,[2] in their discussion of human locomotion, deal first with the kinematics of walking and describe the displacements of the body segments in the three cardinal planes, covering flexion and extension of the thigh and leg, pelvic rotation, and so on. They consider next the kinetics of walking, analyzing the forces of the muscles as well as those of gravity and of floor reaction, all of which are necessary for propulsion of the body and control of segmental displacements.

The basic laws which are involved in the areas of statics, kinematics, and kinetics were formulated near the beginning of the eighteenth century by Sir Isaac Newton, an English mathematician. The principles themselves are quite simple and are readily understood, but their application to the solution of problems may become rather difficult. In order to simplify the approach to problems a special method of attack has been devised and it is the application of this technique that we will be concerned with in this text.

In our discussion, we will make use of two of Newton's three laws (the first and third), which state that:

1. *A body remains at rest or in uniform motion until acted upon by an unbalanced set of forces.* This means that if a body is at rest, the forces acting on it must be completely balanced; the body is then said to be in equilibrium. If a body is moving it will continue to move at a uniform speed until some force causes it to stop moving or to change its rate or direction of motion (Newton's first law).*

2. *For every action there is an equal and opposite reaction.* In any case in which two bodies are in contact, the force exerted on the second body by the first must be exactly *equal* and *opposite* to

---

* Newton's second law is a special case of the first, and states that the acceleration of a particle is proportional to the unbalanced force acting upon it and inversely proportional to the mass of the particle. In other words, a large push on a small object will accelerate it rapidly, and a small push on a large object will accelerate it slowly.

Fig. 1.2. A push must be opposed by an equal and opposite push, as illustrated by the two figures. The equal and opposite push of the wall (P) is not as easy to see but it is just as real.

the force exerted on the first body by the second (Fig. 1.2). If you push against an object it pushes back against you with equal force in a direction exactly opposite to that of your push (Newton's third law).

The reader can think immediately of many instances in which these two laws apply. The first concept, which has been called Newton's *law of inertia,* is well illustrated in normal walking. The lower limb must be swung forward forcibly by action of the hip flexor muscles so that the foot may be placed ahead of the body as the center of gravity travels forward. The leg swing is a ballistic or "thrown" movement which, once begun, continues without further muscle effort. The swinging limb must then be stopped or decelerated in a controlled fashion by the hip extensors so that the heel can be brought to the ground at the proper time and place (Fig. 1.3). Gravity is also a force here in the acceleration of the limb at the beginning of the swing and in deceleration at the end of the swing. This swinging action of the limb in walking is like that of a "damped pendulum" which is forcibly accelerated and then, once started, must be forcibly

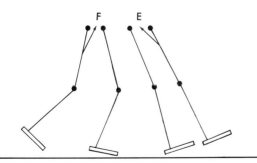

Fig. 1.3. In the ballistic movement of hip flexion during the swing phase of walking, the thigh is first accelerated by the hip flexor muscles (F) at the beginning of swing and then decelerated by the hip extensors (E) before heel strike.

stopped. Without the muscle forces, the limb would continue at rest or continue in motion beyond the proper point, making smooth walking impossible. The control of the arm swing by muscles in fast walking or running is another example of muscle activity used to overcome inertia of a body segment.

A body which is stationary, or moving at a constant speed, is said to be in a state of equilibrium. A force must be applied to change this state. In the case of a moving object, forces which help to slow down and stop the motion include (1) friction between the object and the supporting surface, and (2) air resistance. A patient being moved in a wheel chair may be thrown forward if the wheels suddenly catch on a door sill; or, if someone gives the chair an unexpected shove from behind, the patient's trunk is forced against the back of the chair. We have all had this experience while riding in an automobile when the driver suddenly applied the accelerator or the brake.

The property of matter known as *inertia* causes an object to resist either being set in motion or, if moving, to resist being slowed down or stopped. The inertia of a body is proportional to its weight. If an aide attempts to push a very heavy patient on a guerney it is not only difficult for him to get started but also to stop the movement at the end of the trip. A child being transported would offer less resistance to starting and stopping. Likewise, an amputee need overcome less inertia in the control of the remaining portion of a limb than in control of the normal side. On the other hand, a limb in a cast or brace requires more than normal energy to control. The amount of decrease or increase of inertia is directly proportional to the change in mass. This is an important factor in energy expenditure and fatigue. Compare your own arm swing in walking when your hands are free with your swing when you are carrying a brief case in one hand.

An example of the effect of inertia frequently seen in the clinic is the trauma sustained by the cervical spine in so-called "whiplash" injuries or "cervical syndrome." As the car in such accidents is usually bumped from the rear, the rider's head is first snapped into extension. This is because it tends to remain at rest while the trunk is moved violently forward. The head then is thrown into a flexed position as the trunk comes to rest. In this way the delicate structures on both the anterior and posterior aspects of the neck may be damaged.

Newton's third law, regarding equal and opposite force reactions, is illustrated by the usual floor or ground reaction in standing or walking. The supporting surface pushes upward against the sole of the foot with the same amount of force and along the same line of action as the downward force of the foot (Fig. 1.4). In locomotion the character of the surface may be such that it fails to provide counterforce to the foot and makes progress difficult and tiring, as when one walks on soft sand or gravel. Thin ice may supply the necessary "equal and opposite" reaction for a small boy while his older brother will break through the surface.

If a crutch or cane is placed on the floor in a vertical position it is very stable since the floor pushes vertically upward in return. However, if a crutch is placed far out to the side at an angle to the body, the action line of the reaction force is at a corresponding angle with the vertical, and the crutch is more likely to slip (Fig. 1.5). A person taking long strides is more apt to skid for-

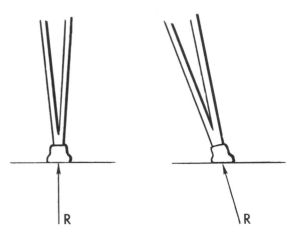

Fig. 1.5. The direction of floor reaction force R is shown. The arrows might be reversed to indicate the direction of the downward force exerted by the crutch.

ward when his heel strikes a slippery floor than one who takes shorter steps with his foot coming down in a more nearly vertical direction.

Horizontal force, such as that which accompanies the push-off in walking, must be opposed by an equal and opposite force so that the foot is stable and progression can take place. Friction between the sole of the foot and the ground normally supplies the necessary counterforce here. Lack of friction, as in walking on a slippery surface, will make normal walking difficult or impossible.

In our daily life, all posture and movement is constantly influenced by the surface which supports us. We may not be conscious of this because through experience our adjustments have become largely automatic. Contrast your movement in stepping off a curb into the street with stepping into a small canoe on a lake. Unfamiliar or unstable supporting surfaces require control of movement on a conscious level. A paraplegic patient may face frustration and possible injury if he attempts to get on a bed which has freely rolling casters, or if he forgets to lock his wheelchair or back it up against the wall before he sits down in it (Fig. 1.6). He cannot plan and execute his movements successfully unless he has adequate counterforce from a stable bed or chair.

A familiar example of equal and opposite reaction of forces is the healthful effect of a firm mattress, which keeps the vertebral column straight, and the evil effect of a sagging one, which allows it to bend. This point is emphasized constantly by the orthopedist in treating

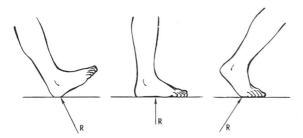

Fig. 1.4. The ground reaction force R is equal in action line and magnitude to the downward thrust of the foot during walking, but opposite in direction. The force is greater at heel-strike than at mid-stance because of the body's momentum, and greater at push-off due to the plantar flexion thrust of the calf muscles driving the body forward.

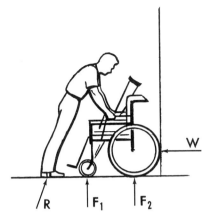

Fig. 1.6. The floor and wall provide counterforce F and W to stabilize the wheelchair as the patient prepares to sit down. (Floor reaction force R is shown also.)

patients with low back pain. Good body alignment is assured also by exercise mats and plinths with surfaces which are comfortable and yet firmly support the body segments. The fitting of lower extremity prostheses which bear weight is another example of force and counterforce in which the shape and firmness of the supporting surface is critical.

Pressure is an important aspect of force and its mode of application.

$$\text{Pressure} = \frac{\text{total force}}{\text{area of force application}}$$

This formula yields average pressure, given in units of force per unit area—for example, pounds per square inch. If a pressure pad on a back brace exerts a 4 pound force over an area 6 × 8 inches, the average pressure in the region beneath the pad would be $\frac{4 \text{ lb.}}{48 \text{ sq. in.}}$ or about 0.083 lb. per square inch. What would be the magnitude of the pressure per unit area if the pad were 3 × 4 inches in size?

This principle of pressure per unit area is utilized in skiing and snowshoeing, making it possible to stand and walk on soft snow (Fig. 1.7). Water skiing is another example, although here forward motion is necessary in combination with a large supporting surface to keep the rider from sinking. A surf board or a small boat will support the body even when it is stationary.

If you push with your fist into the palm of the opposite hand you can withstand considerable force without discomfort. The same amount

of force exerted by your thumb into the palm becomes painful as the pressure per unit area is now much greater. An equal force exerted by the point of a needle would be disastrous. In general, to avoid pain and possible injury to the skin, forces should be sustained over as large as possible an area of body surface. Skin breakdown, pressure sores, and ulcerated areas are serious clinical complications which should never be allowed to happen as a result of carelessness.

The position of bed patients should be changed frequently in order to alternate the skin areas under pressure. This is particularly true in the presence of circulatory or sensory impairment. Pressure is a critical factor in the prosthetic fitting of lower extremity amputees, especially those with ischial weight-bearing devices or end-bearing stumps. The socket must be designed so that the contact force is distributed over a large skin area. Padding of bony prominences is important here as well as in the application of braces and casts.

The "give" or yield of the material contacting and supporting the body surface is a primary factor in avoiding dangerous effects of continuous pressure. When force is exerted against the body surface by rigid materials, such as wood or metal, pressure is concentrated in the area of bony prominences. Softer materials, such as felt

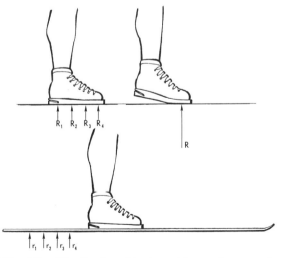

Fig. 1.7. Distribution of body weight on the supporting surface varies according to the surface contact area. R = reacting force of the floor. Picture a toe dancer here; contrast the pressure per unit area with that on the skis. (The pressure shown under one area actually acts over the entire length of the ski surface.)

padding or sponge rubber, allow for better equalization of the pressure over the entire contact area and protect the skin over bony prominences. Equalization of pressure has been attempted by inserting an air-filled chamber or water bag of some sort between the two contacting surfaces. Bremner[3] recently applied this principle in scoliosis bracing by inserting a water-inflated football (Rugby) bladder between a plaster jacket and the thorax at the site of corrective pressure. The advantage of this "hydrostatic bag" was said to be "automatic pressure distribution and perfect congruity and adaptability of shape," particularly in adjusting to breathing and other trunk movements.

Head slings used in neck traction apparatus should fit snugly so that pressure will be applied as evenly as possible over a large surface (Fig. 4.7, p. 28). A tongue blade placed between the teeth will help to distribute pressure between the maxilla and mandible if the patient complains of discomfort.

pendulum as shown in Figure 1.8 (Codman's exercises).

 (1) A weight is held in the patient's hand during these exercises.
(e) A patient who is practicing posture exercises is unable to keep the proper trunk alignment because the table mat is too soft.

Fig. 1.8. Codman's exercises are used to mobilize the shoulder joint with the aid of gravity.

Questions

1. Is an object in equilibrium always stationary? What is the definition of a state of equilibrium in mechanics?

2. Should a description of scapulohumeral rhythm in arm elevation, which disregards the forces involved, be considered in the area of kinetics or kinematics?

3. Explain how one or more of Newton's laws is involved in each of the following:

(a) A patient who is seated stands up.

(b) A patient is practicing a "swing through" crutch gait in which he leans forward on both crutches, swings both legs forward and places his feet on the floor ahead of the crutch tips.

(c) As an exercise weight is hung on a wall peg, the peg supporting the weight breaks off.

 (1) The falling weight smashes a hole through the floor.

(d) In an effort to gain increased range of shoulder motion, a therapist directs the patient to lean forward and swing his arm in various directions in the manner of a

4. Suggest some additional examples of Newton's laws from the clinical area and also from sports (e.g., kicking a football, high jumping).

5. Compare walking with running in terms of Newton's laws.

6. How does the pressure per unit area concept apply to the use of skis and snowshoes? To the size and number of sails on a boat?

7. Compare skin pressure on the sole of the foot in ordinary standing and in tiptoe standing. How does this apply to a patient with an equinus (fixed plantar flexion) deformity of the foot?

8. Why might posture control chairs which fix the body position rigidly be harmful to patients if used for long periods of time?

9. How can the pressure per unit area concept be applied to the analysis of massage techniques such as petrissage and friction? Give examples.

10. How is it possible that a 110-pound woman in walking may exert a pressure of more than one ton per square inch at heel-strike when she wears spike heels?

Bibliography

1. Guthrie-Smith, O. F.; *Rehabilitation, Re-Education and Remedial Exercises.* Baltimore, Williams & Wilkins Co., 1943.
2. Klopsteg, P. E., and Wilson, P. D.: *Human Limbs and their Substitutes.* New York, McGraw-Hill Book Co. Inc., 1954, pp. 455–471.
3. Bremner, R. A.: Observations on the ambulant correction of thoracic scoliosis and kyphosis with particular reference to the experimental use of hydrostatic pressure. *J. Bone Joint Surg. (Brit.), 41*:96–104, 1959.

CHAPTER TWO

Useful Terms and Concepts

Before going into the solution of problems it will be necessary to define certain terms that are used. In mechanics we deal with *force, space, matter,* and *time.*

Force is one of the basic concepts in the subject of mechanics. Everybody knows what a force is, but it is difficult to define. To produce a force it is always necessary for one object or body to act on another. This action may result in a pull (tension) or a push (compression) and, according to Newton's third law, the body being pushed pushes back just as hard on the body doing the pushing. This means, for example, that if you push down on the desk with a force of five pounds the desk is pushing back up against you with a force of five pounds. Forces may also act between bodies at a distance and not in contact with each other. Examples include the attractive force of gravity, the attraction and repulsion of electrically charged particles, or the attractive forces in the nucleus which hold the atom together. Another thing that we know about a force is that it is not completely described if we know only its *magnitude.* A ten pound force acting downward on a table produces an entirely different effect from that of a ten pound force acting on the table in a horizontal direction. Thus in addition to its magni-

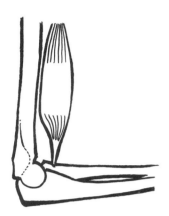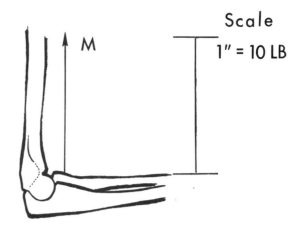

Fig. 2.1. The muscle pull (M) is shown as a vector force drawn to an arbitrarily selected scale: 1 inch = 10 pounds.

tude, the *action line* of the force must be known, and since the effect will be different if we pull instead of push, the *direction* along the action line is also of fundamental importance. Finally, the *point of application* at which the force is applied to the body is of considerable importance as we will see later. These four factors, then, are called the characteristics of a force:

1. Magnitude
2. Action line
3. Direction
4. Point of application

All four of these characteristics must be given to define a force completely. If we are to describe a force applied to the forearm, for example, we must give its magnitude, point of application, action line, and direction in order to have a complete picture. Any variation in any of these characteristics will produce a different result on the forearm.

A force is considered as a *vector quantity* because it has magnitude and direction and thus can be represented by a vector, which is a directed straight line. (A vector quantity differs from a scalar quantity in that a vector represents both magnitude and direction, whereas a scalar quantity represents magnitude only; examples of scalar quantities are fifty cents or three quarts.) When a vector is used to represent a force, its length should be made proportional to the magnitude of the force. If we let one-half inch represent five pounds, a line one inch long would represent a force of ten pounds. Since the vector drawn to scale indicates magnitude (by its length), action line

(by the location of its shaft), and direction of the force (arrow head), and it is placed on the object at the point of application of the force, the vector can be used to define the force completely. For example, in Figure 2.1 a vector is used to represent the force of the biceps muscle. In mechanics we use vectors constantly since this is the easiest way to deal with forces, and the student should become proficient in visualizing force systems as series of vectors acting in relation to an object or to one another. (Any group of two or more forces is known as a *force system*.)

Any time a vector is used to represent a force it should be labeled with a letter or number designating its magnitude as shown in Figure 2.2. If its magnitude in pounds is known we of course label the vector with the actual force in pounds. If, however, the magnitude of the force is unknown, we use a letter such as F or P to designate the magnitude of the force. Capital letters are generally used for this purpose.

In order to use vectors properly, they must

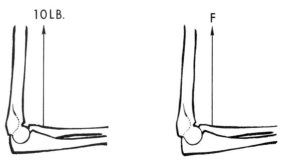

Fig. 2.2. Vectors should always be identified by a label indicating magnitude.

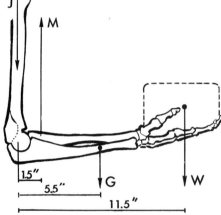

Fig. 2.3. The forearm and hand supporting a weight are shown with the forces represented by vectors, where

M = force of flexor muscle
G = gravitational pull on forearm
W = weight held in the hand
J = force of humerus against ulna

Distances are indicated between elbow joint axis and the location of various forces along the forearm.

be located accurately on the body or object on which the forces are acting. Since the object or body may be rather complicated, we can represent it by a simplified drawing called a *space* or *line diagram*. Only enough details are required on the line diagram to locate properly the position of the forces. Drawing of the line diagram in some cases is quite simple while in other cases it becomes more difficult. A line diagram must contain the necessary dimensions to locate accurately the position of all forces acting on the body. Distances may be designated in actual values, if known, or by small letters; use inches with pounds, or centimeters with grams or kilograms (Fig. 2.3).

Space is another basic consideration in the study of mechanics. The forces that we deal with may act along a single line, in a single plane, or in any direction in space. Since we

must have some means of locating our forces along a line, in a plane, or in space, it is necessary to provide some reference system. We do this by dividing the plane into four quadrants by means of two perpendicular lines or axes. These axes are generally labeled X in the horizontal direction and Y in the vertical direction. (The X axis is termed the abscissa, the Y axis the ordinate.) The point of intersection of the two axes is known as the *origin* of the system. Measurements to the right of and above the origin are positive and those to the left and below are negative (Fig. 2.4). Any point on the plane can now be defined by being assigned an X and Y number. The point A defined by X = 3, Y = 5, will be found three units to the right of the origin and five units above the origin. The point B, defined by X = −4, Y = 2, is found by going four units to the left of the origin and up two units.

In order to locate points in space outside the original plane, a third axis must be introduced. This passes through the origin and perpendicular to the X–Y plane in which the two original axes are found. The third axis is usually labeled Z. All points in front of the original X–Y plane are positive, while those behind the X–Y plane are negative. Now we have the means of locating any point in space. After the position in the X–Y plane is defined, we can locate the point either in front of the plane or behind the plane

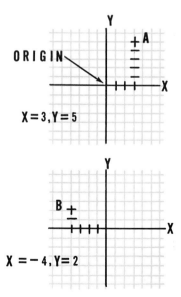

Fig. 2.4. Points may be located in a plane in relation to X and Y axes.

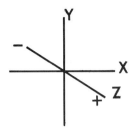

Fig. 2.5. Addition of the Z axis to the X and Y coordinates permits location of points in space.

by means of a positive or negative Z coordinate (Fig. 2.5).

In setting up such a system of coordinates for the purpose of describing human motion, it is convenient to place the origin at the center of gravity of the body, which is approximately anterior to the second sacral vertebra. Three cardinal planes may then be visualized in relation to the X, Y, and Z coordinates (Fig. 2.6):

Frontal (or coronal) dividing the body into front and back portions (X–Y plane);

Sagittal dividing the body into right and left halves (Y–Z plane);

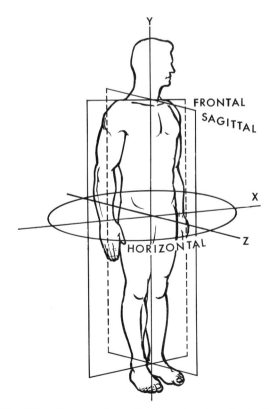

Fig. 2.6. System of coordinates related to the body; the origin is at the body's center of gravity, anterior to the second sacral vertebra.

Transverse (or horizontal) dividing the body into upper and lower portions (X–Z plane).

This system of reference coordinates and planes facilitates description of movements of the body segments and allows for an exact definition of any point in space. Adolph Fick,[1] who first computed the action of the thigh muscles on the hip joint a little over a hundred years ago, used such a system. Since he was interested in muscle action relative to the hip joint, he placed the origin of his coordinate system at the axis of the joint as shown in Figure 2.7. By projecting the action lines of the individual muscles, he could determine their effect in moving the femur in each of the three cardinal planes. For example, a muscle such as the iliacus or pectineus, pulling in a direction anterior to the X–Y plane, flexes the part. The gluteus maximus, pulling posterior to this plane, extends it. The adductor and abductor muscles apply their force from points medial and lateral (respectively) to the Y–Z plane. Rotation is calculated in relation to the Y axis. (The means of computing the values of muscle forces such as these will be considered in Chapter 6.) The method employed by Fick to determine the action of muscles about the center of rotation of a joint has been in general use for many years.

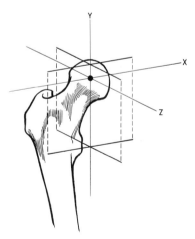

Fig. 2.7. System of coordinates related to the mechanical axis of the hip joint.

Elaborate globe-shaped devices have been made to measure the position of the body segments in space and to record ranges of motion in joints which move in two or more planes (Fig. 2.8). A number of examples are cited by Steindler.[2] For the purpose of kinematic analysis

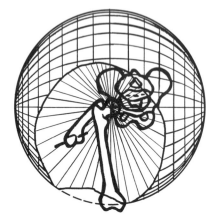

Fig. 2.8. Example of "globographic" recording of range of joint motion (from Strasser).

of movements of the upper extremity, Taylor and Blaschke[3] have worked out a complex system of angles, axes, and centers. These authors stress that even this elaborate method is somewhat idealized and only approximates the true joint function which is rather complicated.

Matter is that which occupies space. In our discussion of biomechanics we will often be dealing with a unit of matter, or mass,* to which the force of gravity is applied. This mass may be an object, such as an exercise weight, or it may be the entire body or a segment of the body. In order to apply the principles of mechanics to human movement, the concept of *center of gravity* of an object must be used constantly. This is a point at the exact center of its mass. In the case of a square block or a cylinder, in which the mass is symmetrically distributed, this point is at the geometric center of the object (Fig. 2.9).

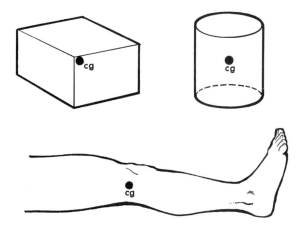

Fig. 2.9. Center of mass of symmetrical and asymmetrical objects.

However, if the distribution of mass is asymmetrical, as is true of the limbs of the human body, the center of gravity will be nearer to the larger and heavier end.

The center of gravity of the entire human body, when the limbs are straight as in ordinary standing, lies within the pelvis (Fig. 2.10). This point may vary in position from person to person according to body build, age, and sex. It will also vary within any given person when the arrangement of the segments shifts as in walking, running, or in the sitting position. Since this point represents the center of the total mass, it will shift when weight is added to or subtracted from some part of the body, as with the addition of a cast or brace, or following amputation of an extremity. Weights and centers of

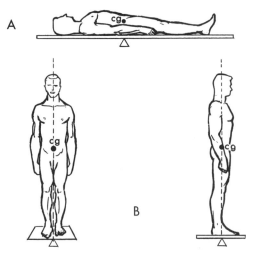

Fig. 2.10. Center of gravity of the body and its vertical projection; body is balanced over the base of support in three positions.

gravity of the body segments have been determined by Braune and Fischer[4] and more recently by Dempster.[5] Dempster's data are given in the appendix and will be useful in estimating the magnitude and location of gravitational forces as accurately as possible in setting up and solving problems. A summary of useful data is given in Figure 2.11.

The important thing to remember is that *a*

* The units of mass are $\frac{\text{lb. sec.}^2}{\text{ft.}}$. This follows from Newton's second law, $F = Ma$, where F is pounds weight, M is mass, a is acceleration in ft./sec.^{2}, and $M = \frac{F}{a} = \frac{\text{lb. sec.}^2}{\text{ft.}}$.

rigid object behaves as if its entire mass were acting (or being acted upon) at its center of gravity. A book may be pushed far out over the edge of a table but it will not topple off until its center of gravity is no longer supported (Fig. 2.12). In other words, the object behaves as if gravitational pull concentrates its entire force at this single point. In the case of the book, the object will fall as soon as its center of gravity passes over the table edge even though a large part of the mass is still supported. This demonstrates the importance of the base of support to the stability of the object. In order for an object to remain upright, a vertical line projected downward from its center of gravity must fall within the area of support. If the line falls outside this area the object will topple over (Fig. 2.13).

Increasing the area of the base of support will increase stability. The upright human body is least stable when the feet are parallel and close together. As the feet are moved apart and the base is broadened, the person becomes less likely to fall (Fig. 2.14). Recall the wide stance assumed by persons standing on a moving bus, or on the deck of a ship which is pitching and tossing. In ordinary standing positions the center of gravity of the body is constantly shifting slightly, primarily in an anteroposterior direction.[6] This postural sway, which normally is under the control of automatic neuromuscular mechanisms, necessitates an adequate base area. The use of a crutch or cane will greatly increase the stability of a patient. In Figure 2.15 stable and unstable stance on crutches is illustrated.

When a person stoops or reaches, he usually advances one foot to broaden the supporting area. A broad base in the direction of body movement is essential in such activities as giving massage and in assistance and support of a patient who is walking or rising from or being seated in a chair.[7] Stability of the therapist is vital to safety as well as to ease of movement. In supporting or lifting a patient the therapist may add a considerable portion of the patient's weight to his own. In this case we must consider the center of gravity of the combined mass of both persons.

Two familiar stunts illustrate how the center of gravity shifts with a change in posture and how it is necessary to balance the weight over the feet. Ask a friend to stand with his back to a wall and his heels touching or as close to the wall as he can get them. Place a dollar on the floor in front of him and tell him that it is his if he can lean over and pick it up without moving his feet. Of course this is impossible as he must either move one foot forward to provide a base beneath his center of gravity or he must shift his trunk backward to balance over his feet, which is prevented by the wall. A similar impossible feat is to stand facing the edge of a door which is ajar, place the forefeet on either side so that abdomen and nose are touching the door's edge, and rise on tiptoe. Why can this not be done?

When a person carries a heavy weight, the body shifts in the opposite direction in order to compensate; in this way the center of gravity of the combined mass is maintained in a central position over the feet (Fig. 2.16). The opposite arm is automatically lifted to help counterbalance a very heavy load held in one hand. A load carried as near as possible to the midline of the body will minimize the necessary realignment of body segments and consequent muscle and ligament strain.

Balancing the center of gravity of the body over the feet requires no conscious thought or effort for the ordinary person. However, for patients with spinal cord lesions and many other types of muscle weakness of the trunk and lower limbs, body balance becomes a critical problem. The slightest miscalculation may result in a fall. The paraplegic patient must learn to master the delicate interplay in position between his pelvis and his head and shoulders. When one of these segments moves forward the other must move backward to compensate, and vice versa. Since he retains muscular control of the head and shoulder position, he can move this mass to help place the pelvis where he wants it to go in ambulation, stair climbing, and so on. He throws his head backward or forward to assist in moving and placing the lower trunk mass. Control of this fine interplay of position of these body segments is the key to basic posture and movement of the paraplegic. To assist and instruct the patient, the physical therapist must analyze the mechanics involved in segmental balance, in both resting and moving postures (Fig. 2.17). An excellent application of the interplay of head and pelvic positions in the movement of normal persons is in diving, where the position of the body "follows the lead" of the head.

14

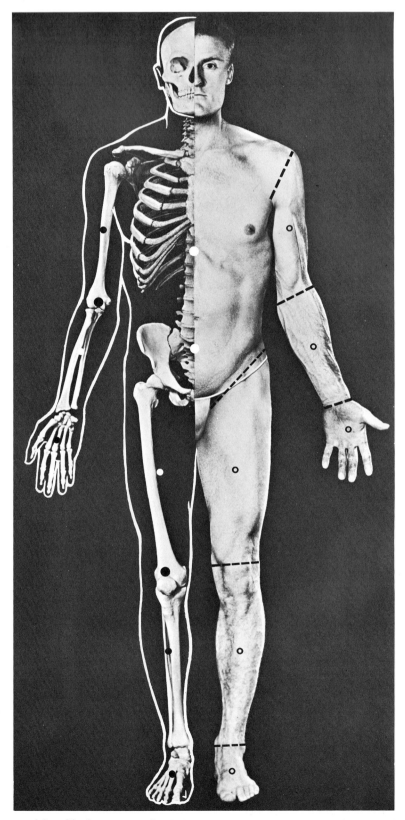

Fig. 2.11. Average weight of body segments for 150 pound man and percentage of total body weight; center of gravity loci (based on Dempster, *op. cit.,* pp. 129 to 135). Original data are on p. 135. Value for head weight was computed from Braune and Fischer's data. Center of gravity loci are from Dempster except those for entire limbs and body. (See opposite page.)

SEGMENT WEIGHTS AND PERCENTAGE OF TOTAL BODY WEIGHT FOR 150 POUND MAN.	LOCATION OF CENTERS OF GRAVITY
Head: 10.3 lb. (6.9%)	*Head.* In sphenoid sinus, 4 mm. beyond anterior inferior margin of sella. (On lateral surface, over temporal fossa on or near nasion-inion line).
Head and neck: 11.8 lb. (7.9%)	*Head and neck.* On inferior surface of basioccipital bone or within bone 23 ± 5 mm. from crest of dorsum sellae. (On lateral surface, 10 mm. anterior to supratragic notch above head of mandible.)
Head, neck and trunk: 88.5 lb. (59.0%)	*Head, neck and trunk.* Anterior to eleventh thoracic vertebra.

UPPER LIMB. Just above elbow joint.

Arm: 4.1 lb. (2.7%)	*Arm.* In medial head of triceps, adjacent to radial groove; 5 mm. proximal to distal end of deltoid insertion.
Forearm: 2.4 lb. (1.6%)	*Forearm.* 11 mm. proximal to most distal part of pronator teres insertion; 9 mm. anterior to interosseus membrane.
Hand: 0.9 lb. (0.6%)	*Hand.* (in rest position). On axis of metacarpal III, usually 2 mm. deep to volar skin surface. 2 mm. proximal to proximal transverse palmar skin crease, in angle between proximal transverse and radial longitudinal crease.
Upper limb: 7.3 lb. (4.9%)	
Forearm and hand: 3.3 lb. (2.2%)	

LOWER LIMB. Just above knee joint.

Thigh: 14.5 lb. (9.7%)	*Thigh.* In adductor brevis muscle (or magnus or vastus medialis) 13 mm. medial to linea aspera, deep to adductor canal. 29 mm. below apex of femoral triangle and 18 mm. proximal to most distal fibers of adductor brevis.
Leg: 6.8 lb. (4.5%)	*Leg.* 35 mm. below popliteus, at posterior part of posterior tibialis; 16 mm. above proximal end of Achilles tendon; 8 mm. posterior to interosseus membrane.
Foot: 2.1 lb. (1.4%)	*Foot.* In plantar ligaments, or just superficial in adjacent deep foot muscles; below proximal halves of second and third cuneiform bones. On a line between ankle joint center and ball of foot in plane of metatarsal II.
Lower limb: 23.4 lb. (15.6%)	
Leg and foot: 9.0 lb. (6.0%)	

ENTIRE BODY. Anterior to second sacral vertebra.

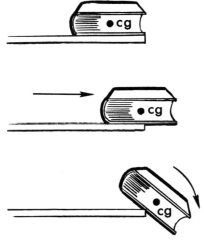

Fig. 2.12. Stability depends on relation of center of gravity to the base of support.

Another type of motor disability in which body balance plays a critical role is muscular dystrophy. In the absence of strength in trunk muscles, the patient arches his spine in an exaggerated lordosis and balances in the upright position. Since the slightest touch may disturb his precarious position, it may be best for the therapist not to attempt to assist him. Walking is slow, requiring a new delicately centered position of balance over each supporting foot after it has swung forward. Here the patient often holds the therapist's arm for support.[8]

Speed of movement is closely associated with requirements for balance. It is easier to balance on a bicycle when it is moving fast than when it is traveling slowly. In the same fashion, patients with a precarious sense of balance may

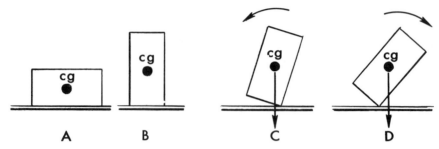

Fig. 2.13. An object is most stable when its center of gravity is low. The object in C will fall back into place and remain vertical; in D, where the center of gravity is not over the base, the object will topple over.

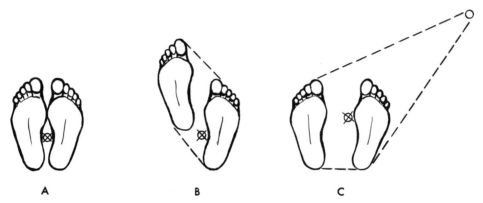

Fig. 2.14. The position of the feet determines the size of the supporting area beneath the body. Use of a cane greatly extends the base of support (C) and the area over which the body is stable.

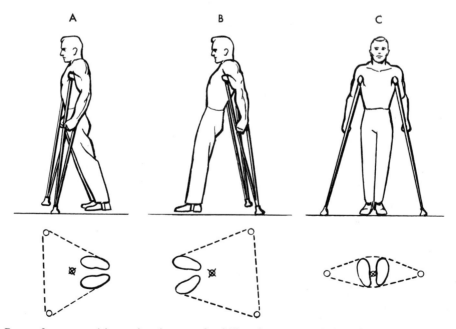

Fig. 2.15. Bases of support with varying degrees of stability. Can you rank these from most stable to least stable? The subject in A and B is secure primarily in the anteroposterior direction; the position in C provides more stability in the frontal plane than in the sagittal plane.

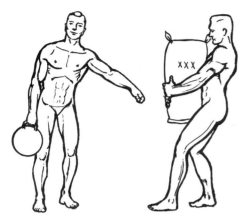

Fig. 2.16. Automatic postural mechanisms normally center the total mass over the base of support when a load is carried.

hurry along in order to decrease the requirements for lateral stability. It may be difficult for some patients to slow down their rate of ambulation, and it may even be helpful to some patients to move a little faster if this can be done with safety.

In certain postures of the body, the center of gravity may lie in space outside the body itself. If this seems strange to you, remember that the center of gravity of a doughnut, located at the center of its mass, must lie in the middle of the hole. When a person leans forward to pick up an object from the floor, his center of mass may be displaced to a point anterior to the trunk

(although it is still over the feet). The center of gravity also moves forward when one is in a sitting position (Fig. 5.36, p. 55). This explains why one is pitched forward if he sits too far out on the front of a folding chair seat. Compare the areas of floor support beneath a wheel chair (four wheels) and a conventional straight chair (four legs). Note what wheel chairs are designed for maximum stability.

In the case of a segmented or linked part, such as an upper or lower limb, the center of the entire part can be computed from the centers of the component segments. When a linked limb is flexed, the single center may be found outside the limb (Fig. 2.18). Here it is helpful to remember that this single center will always lie on a line joining the individual centers of two component segments and thus can be estimated rather accurately.

Note that the *mass* of a body or of a segmented part does not change with a change in its position, but only the location of its center of gravity changes. The only way the mass itself is altered is by amputation or by adding weight to the part as with a shoe, cast, brace, or exercise load.

In summary, since a rigid object behaves as though its entire mass were acting at its center of gravity, it is at this point that we must locate the vector representing the weight of the segment (or total body, depending on what we are dealing with). Such a vector in a line diagram

Fig. 2.17.
A. Manual control of pelvic and upper trunk alignment in ambulation training. Note the position of the therapist's feet.
B. As the patient "climbs up" her crutches in rising to her feet, the therapist helps to keep her pelvis directly over her feet.

A   B

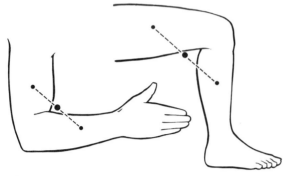

Fig. 2.18. Location of the single center of gravity of linked segments which are flexed.

indicates the force of gravitational pull on the mass. Thus, for example, in the case of an outstretched arm (Fig. 2.19), the four characteristics of the force which is pulling downward on the arm are:

Magnitude: here W = 8 pounds, or approximately 5 per cent of the body weight. (About how much does the man in Figure 2.19 weigh?)

Action line: vertical
Direction: downward

⎧ gravity acts at all times straight downward toward the center of the earth.

Point of application: center of gravity of the limb, which is just above the elbow. ("W" acts at distance "a" from the shoulder.)

It is convenient to visualize the force of gravity acting on a moving part as a plumb line suspended from the center of gravity of the part. In this way the action line and direction of the force will always be properly depicted—vertical

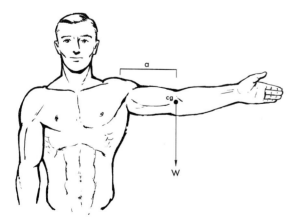

Fig. 2.19. Characteristics of gravitational force on the upper limb (see text). Might this diagram differ if the individual weighed 200 lb.?

and downward. The length of the line, considered as a vector, always represents the weight of the part. Figure 2.20 shows a line diagram of arm elevation with a vector representing gravitational pull acting at the center of gravity. In this instance, as the arm moves upward, the angle it forms with the trunk constantly changes. The angle formed by the arm and the action line of gravity also changes. Therefore the distance from the joint axis at the shoulder to the action line of gravitational pull constantly changes as the arm is elevated, and this distance is maximal when the arm is horizontal.

The exercise loads provided by body weight during four posture exercises are shown in a series of line diagrams in Figure 2.21. Extend each drawing in the series by making similar line diagrams with the segments in other positions during the exercise.

Time does not require an exact definition for purposes of this text.

Questions

1. If a quantity has only magnitude but not direction is it a vector or a scalar quantity? Give an example of a vector quantity; a scalar quantity.

2. What are the four characteristics of a force which are necessary to define the force completely?

   (a) Describe (by a diagram) the pull of the brachialis muscle on the forearm in terms of these four characteristics.

   (b) Describe (by a diagram) the pull of gravity on the forearm in these terms: (1) with the forearm hanging at the side; (2) with the forearm horizontal.

3. Describe a force system (of at least three forces) acting on the forearm. Diagram the system.

4. Make a line drawing of the following:

   (a) forces on the foot as the heel strikes the ground in walking, including:

      (1) the upward force of the ground against the heel

      (2) the downward thrust of the tibia on the talus

      (3) the upward pull of the anterior tibial muscle undergoing eccentric contraction (doing negative work).

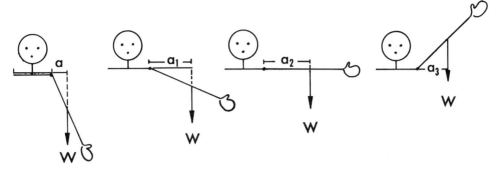

Fig. 2.20. The action line of gravity does not change its direction as the arm is elevated or lowered. It does move outward or inward from the trunk but always remains vertical. (What are the four characteristics of gravitational force on the limb? Do any of them change as the arm is elevated and lowered?)

(b) forces acting on the foot as it pushes off in late stance, including:

(1) the upward pull of the Achilles tendon

(2) the downward thrust of the tibia on the talus

(3) the upward force of the ground against the metatarsal heads.

(c) forces acting on the arm when the patient has flexed it to 90 degrees; include:

(1) the pull of the deltoid acting at the deltoid tubercle

(2) the pull of gravity on the arm (locate the vector at the estimated center of gravity)

(3) the counterforce exerted by the glenoid fossa against the articular surface of the humerus (Newton's third law).

5. What is the origin of a space system? Try to define it in your own words. Review the cardinal axes and planes.

6. Why is the center of gravity of a 3-foot pipe located at its midpoint, while this is not true of either the upper or lower limb of the body?

7. Where is the center of gravity of the human body in the anatomical position and how does it shift when the subject sits down? Account for this shift.

8. How would the location of the center of gravity in the body be changed after an above-knee amputation?

9. According to Dempster's data, how much does one of your own upper limbs weigh? One lower limb? Your head?

10. Locate on yourself and then show by a line diagram where the center of gravity of the upper extremity might be expected to lie:

(a) with the limb fully extended

(b) with the elbow flexed to 90 degrees

(1) On each diagram draw a vector representing the pull of gravity on the arm.

(2) Draw vectors representing the pull of the deltoid and supraspinatus muscles.

Would making a fist or extending the fingers affect the location of the center of gravity of the extremity? How?

11. Compare the relative pressure on the hands when crutches are used as shown in

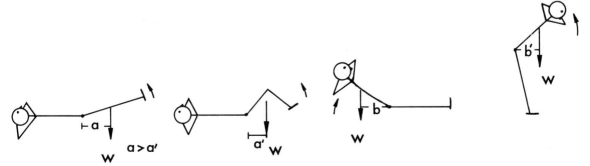

Fig. 2.21. Line diagrams of four posture exercises in which the body segments serve as exercise loads.

Figure 2.15, p. 16. Why does the hand pressure differ?

12. Why is it not possible to sit upright in a chair and rise to one's feet without first leaning forward? What implications has this fact for the design of chairs? For the handling of patients with trunk and lower limb muscle weakness?

Bibliography

1. Fick, A.; Statische Berachtung der Muskulature des Oberschenkels. *Zeitschrift für Rationelle Medicin, 9*:94–106, 1850.
2. Steindler, A.; *Kinesiology.* Springfield, Ill. Charles C Thomas, 1955, pp. 101–119.
3. Taylor, C. L., and Blaschke, A. C.; A method for kinematic analysis of the shoulder, arm and hand complex. *Ann. N. Y. Acad. Sci., 51*: 1123, 1951.
4. Braune, W., and Fischer, O.; Über den Schwerpunkt des Menschlichen Körpers mit Ruchsicht auf die Ausrustung des deutschen Infanteristem. *Abh. D. K. Sachs Ges. d. Wiss.,* vol. 15, part 2, 1889.
5. Dempster, W.; Space requirements of the seated operator. *WADC Technical Report, 55*: 159, 1955.
6. Hellebrandt, F. A., and Fries, E. C.; The constancy of oscillograph stance patterns. *Physiol. Rev., 23*:220–225, 1942.
7. Williams, M., and Worthingham, C.; *Therapeutic Exercise for Body Alignment and Function.* Philadelphia, W. B. Saunders Co., 1957, p. 101.
8. Wratney, M. J.; Physical therapy for muscular dystrophy children. *Phys. Ther. Rev., 38*:26–32, 1958.

CHAPTER THREE

Classification of Force System

We have now been introduced to the representation of forces and force systems by vectors and the setting up of simplified line drawings of force problems. The next step is to examine possible combinations of forces with a view to classifying them into separate systems.

Four such systems will be discussed and these will be considered in the order of their complexity. These four systems are further divided into forces in a plane and forces in space. In this text we will deal with forces in a plane. The four classifications of force systems are:

1. *Linear,* in which all the forces occur along the same action line, as in a tug of war (Fig. 3.1).

Many simple force situations fall into this category, such as a pocket book or brief case held in the hand, a book lying on a table (Fig. 3.2), or a toe dancer standing on tiptoe. According to Newton's third law, in these examples the downward force will be opposed by an equal upward force whose action line is identical with that of the original force. Thus we have a linear system of forces in which the solution of problems is not complicated.

21

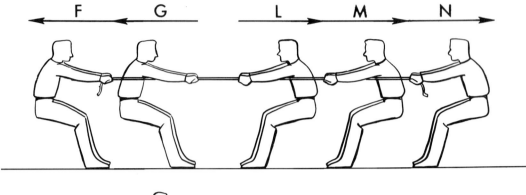

Fig. 3.1.   Forces F, G, and L, M, N are tension forces acting on the rope; R is the equal and opposite force of the rope pulling on the man.

2. *Parallel,* with all the forces parallel and occuring in the same plane but not along the same action line.

Two children on a teeter-totter exert downward forces which are parallel to one another. Their combined weights must be opposed by the upward force at the axis of the board (Fig. 3.3).

In the category of parallel force systems we can place many problems involving forces acting on a segment at various points. These are often: (1) downward forces due to the pull of gravity on the body parts and on supported loads, and (2) upward forces of muscles opposing gravitational pull (Fig. 3.4).

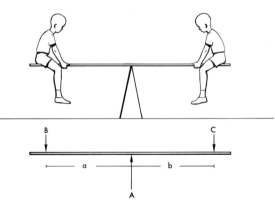

Fig. 3.3.   Here the forces are on opposite sides of the axis; B tends to turn the board in a counter clockwise direction, and C to turn it clockwise. In equilibrium, B + C (downward forces) = A (upward force).

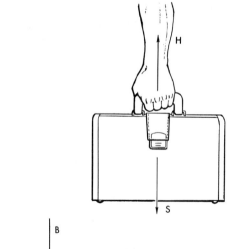

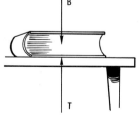

Fig. 3.2.   Simple linear force systems. H = S (forces of hand and bag) and B = T (book and table).

This type of problem becomes more complicated than the linear system, because not only the magnitude of the opposing forces but also their location with respect to the object concerned must be considered.

3. *Concurrent,* in which all the forces meet at a point.

Various traction devices provide examples of this arrangement of forces. In the illustration

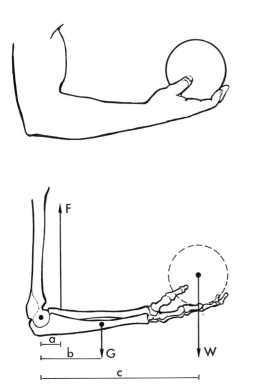

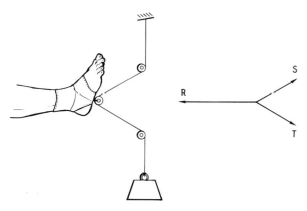

Fig. 3.4. System of forces acting on the forearm, measured from the elbow axis. Forces F, G and W act at distances a, b and c respectively.

(Fig. 3.5) the tension lines converge at the sole of the foot and their combined force is opposed by a force acting cephalad through the leg. That is, the leg "pulls back" against the pulley lines.

By a technique known as resolution of forces these problems can be simplified and solved by a method similar to that used for the linear system.

4. *General*, with the forces in a plane but not

Fig. 3.5. Leg traction with weights. S and T exert a force on the leg equal to R.

in any of the previous arrangements described.

As an example, a patient with a low back disability is resting supine in bed with pelvic traction applied by means of a belt around the trunk (Fig. 3.6). His body weight exerts a downward force (W) opposed by the force of the bed acting upward (N). The pull of the traction apparatus (P) on the body toward the foot of the bed is opposed by the friction (F) between the person's body and the sheet. This friction must be sufficient to keep him from being pulled toward the foot of the bed if the traction is to be effective.

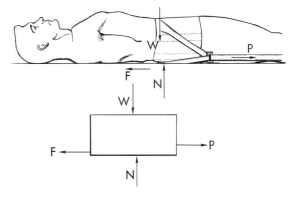

Fig. 3.6. Pelvic traction applied to a bed patient. W = weight of patient; N = reacting force of bed; P = traction force toward feet; F = frictional forces preventing the patient from being pulled downward toward the foot of the bed by the traction belt and weights.

In considering problems in each of the foregoing categories, there are two broad general problems which form the basis for the subject of statics.

1. The first type of problem involves finding the *resultant* of a force system. This is the simplest force or system of forces which will replace a more complex system of forces acting on a body or on a portion of it. Frequently the resultant is a single force or it may be a "couple" (two parallel forces equal in magnitude but applied in opposite directions.)

2. The other basic problem is called the *equilibrium problem*. In it we start with a body known to be at rest and having certain known forces acting on it. To find a solution we determine those forces acting on it which are unknown. For example, suppose you are in a shoulder exercise class, standing with your feet 6 inches apart, and holding a 10 pound weight in each hand at your side. Without moving the rest of

your body you now abduct your left arm to the horizontal position, still holding the weight. You weigh 105 pounds. Find the force between each foot and the ground. This is an equilibrium problem since the body under consideration is at rest and the unknown forces acting on the soles of the feet are to be determined. (We will solve this later.)

Finally, two types of solution are possible for each type of problem we have mentioned: (1) graphic and (2) algebraic. We will use both methods in solving problems.

The classification of force systems, types of basic problems, and the possible methods of their solution will be clarified by examples in the sections to follow.

Summary

CLASSIFICATION OF FORCE SYSTEMS	TYPES OF BASIC PROBLEMS	POSSIBLE METHODS OF SOLUTION
1. Linear 2. Parallel 3. Concurrent 4. General	1. Finding the Resultant or 2. The Equilibrium Problem	1. Graphic or 2. Algebraic

CHAPTER FOUR

The Linear Force System

In the first and simplest of the four force systems to be considered, the linear system, all the forces have the same action line. It is not difficult to think of examples. For instance, a person standing on one foot, supported by the upward thrust of the floor, demonstrates a linear force system. A lamp resting on a table is another example.

In the clinic, Sayre sling suspension, some arrangements of skeletal traction, and many pulley weight exercise devices fall into this classification. A series of exercise weights loaded on a weight pan or hanging on a storage peg constitutes a linear force system. Their total force would obviously be determined by adding them together, and the opposing force of the weight pan or peg would have to be equal to the total sum of the weights. A patient preparing for deLorme boot exercises for the quadriceps muscles may sit with his leg over the edge of the plinth while the exercise load is applied (Fig. 4.1). Before the beginning of the exercise, if the foot is dangling, the ligaments of the knee are obliged to support the total weight of the leg, the boot, and the applied weights. When a walking cast or brace is applied to the foot these exert an added downward force which must be opposed by the ligaments

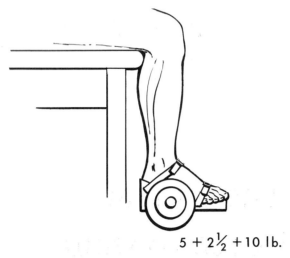

$5 + 2\frac{1}{2} + 10$ lb.

Fig. 4.1. Patient with deLorme boot at the beginning of quadriceps exercise. The downward force of the leg, boot, and exercise weight exerts tension on the supporting structures of the knee joint.

and muscles passing across each of the lower extremity joints which is proximal to the cast. In this case the longitudinal tension on the structures of each joint involved equals the weight of the distal part plus the added weight of the cast or brace.

As was mentioned earlier, often an exact computation of forces is not necessary for clinical purposes. However, for clarity and to illustrate steps in procedure, a series of problems will be presented for solution. Let us consider first some problems which can be solved by finding a *resultant force*. Remember that the selection of the approach to a problem is determined by the nature of the question and by the data given. Both algebraic and graphic methods should be used in arriving at the answer. This serves as a check on accuracy.

Finding a Resultant Force

1. Problem

A deLorme boot is loaded with a 5 lb. weight, a 2½ lb. weight, and a 10 lb. weight. The boot and bar together weigh 2½ lb.

QUESTION. What is the magnitude of the single equivalent force?

SOLUTION. (1) *Algebraic.* Since all the weights are acting in the same direction along the same

action line, their values may be added together:

$$R = 5 + 2\frac{1}{2} + 10 + 2\frac{1}{2} = 20 \text{ lb.}$$
(This is a tension force.)

(2) *Graphic.* A vector diagram of the forces is drawn (Fig. 4.2). To do this we place each force individually in line with its original position. Starting with the first force, we represent it by a line whose length corresponds to 5 lb. If ½ in. = 5 lb. in our scale, this line must be ½ in. long. An arrow head at one end of the line indicates the direction in which the force is acting. We then select a second force—it doesn't matter which one—and draw it in line with the first, starting it at the arrow tip of the preceding force and drawing it in the direction it is actually going. As it is going in the same direction as the first force in this case, the original line is extended by the amount of the second force. This process is repeated for all the forces given.

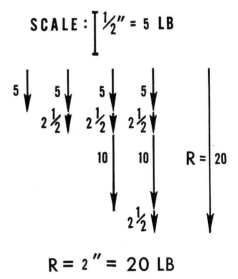

Fig. 4.2. Graphic solution to problem 1. The vector representing 5 lb. is drawn first; the 2½ lb., 10 lb., and 2½ lb. forces, each drawn to scale, are added in turn to find R.

The resultant force, or that force having exactly the same effect as all the forces acting together, is determined by a line drawn from the tail or beginning of the first force to the arrow tip of the last. It is essential that this order be followed, as this gives us the direction of the resultant force as well as its magnitude. In the present problem the line representing the resultant force is found to be ½ + ¼ + 1 + ¼

= 2 inches in length, representing 20 lb. of force according to the scale selected (½ in. = 5 lb.; thus 2 in. = 20 lb.).

This answer verifies the algebraic solution. An excellent practice in all problems in mechanics is to use some check on the original result.

2. Problem

A 145 lb. man puts his ½ lb. hat on his head (Fig. 4.3).

QUESTION. What is the total superincumbent force on the first cervical vertebra?

SOLUTION. (1) *Algebraic.* Since the weights are acting in the same direction along the same action line, their values may be added. According to our data on page 15, the man's head weighs .069 × 145 = 10 lb. Thus the total superincumbent force is:

$$R = 10 + ½ = 10½ \text{ lb.}$$

Fig. 4.3. Load on first cervical vertebra, problem 2. H = downward force of head and hat, opposed by C, the reacting force of the supporting first cervical vertebra. In the graphic solution, H = 10½ lb.

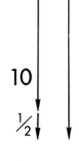

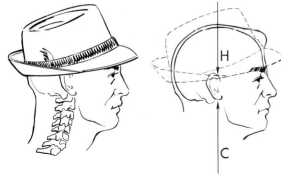

(2) *Graphic.* A vector diagram with a scale 1 in. = 2 lb. might be used. Vectors of ¼ in. and 5 in. are drawn, totaling 5¼ in. According to our scale, this represents 10½ lb. Thus, according to Newton's third law, the first cervical vertebra must provide an upward push of this magnitude in order to support the head and the hat.

*   *   *

In the next few problems pulleys are used. Two basic points regarding pulleys are important:

(1) A single pulley changes the direction but not the magnitude of the force in the pulley rope (Fig. 4.4). The force remains the same on either side of the pulley; thus it follows that,

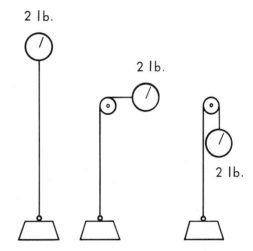

Fig. 4.4. A single pulley changes the direction of the force; it does not change its magnitude (except for reducing it slightly because of friction).

(2) In a pulley system anchored at one end with a force applied to the other end, the force in any strand is equal to that in each of the other strands. In other words, the force in each strand is equivalent to the force applied to the system—usually a weight hung on the end of the rope (Fig. 4.5).

In the following examples we will ignore the friction introduced into the system by the pulleys.

3. Problem

Traction is applied to a leg in line with the tibia by 5 lb. and 10 lb. weights suspended on

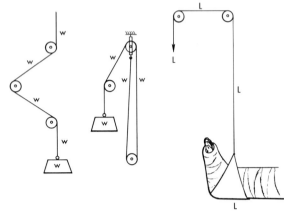

Fig. 4.5.   The tension in the rope in all parts of a pulley system is the same (equal to the traction weight). Thus two or three parallel strands will double or triple the traction force. (Conversely, with two or three strands the traction weight may be reduced by half or two-thirds and still have the same effect.) A single strand, L, supports the leg and cast.

a rope which passes over a single pulley (Fig. 4.6A).

QUESTION.   What is the traction load applied to the leg?

SOLUTION.   (1) *Algebraic.*

R = 5 + 10 = 15 lb.

Tension in any part of the rope is 15 lb.
(2) *Graphic.* Figure 4.6A; Scale 1 in. = 5 lb.
The traction load on the leg may be doubled

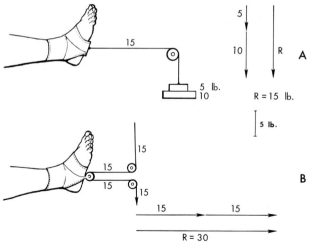

Fig. 4.6.   A. Leg traction: one rope in line with the leg. (R = 15 lb.)
B. Leg traction: two ropes in line with the leg, doubling the traction force. (R = 30 lb.)

by altering the pulley arrangement so that two strands exert a force in line with the leg (Fig. 4.6B). The force at either end of the rope, however, where it is attached to the bed frame above and to the weight pan below, and in all parts of the rope, remains 15 pounds.

The forces in a linear force system may be acting in opposite directions rather than all in the same direction. For example,

4. Problem

A Sayre sling is suspended by a block and tackle system. The lower pulley, weighing 2½ lb., is supported by the strands of the pulley system (Fig. 4.7).

QUESTION.   How much lift is applied to the patient if the therapist pulls on the rope with a force of 15 lb.?

SOLUTION.   We will ignore friction and remember that a single pulley changes the direction but not the magnitude of the force in the pulley rope. Therefore the force in each of the three supporting strands is 15 lb.

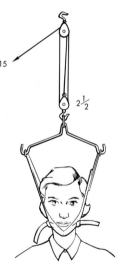

Fig. 4.7.   Sayre traction, with three strands exerting an upward force on the patient's head and neck. While the therapist applying the traction has an advantage of three in force, he must pull the end of the rope through a distance three times as great as the distance through which the head moves.

(1) *Algebraic.* All the forces in one direction are given a positive sign, in this case let us say the upward forces, and all the forces in the opposite direction are given a negative sign. The resultant is obtained by adding all the positive forces and subtracting all the negative forces.

R = 15 + 15 + 15 − 2½ = 42½ lb.

The magnitude of the resultant is determined by the difference between the two sets of figures, and its *direction* is determined by the sign of the answer. Its action line is always identical with that of the original forces. In this problem the weight of the lower pulley is opposed to the upward pull of the ropes; therefore the resultant or single force which will do the same job as all four forces that are acting in the block and tackle system is an upward force (+) of 42½ pounds.

(2) *Graphic.* Figure 4.8; Scale 1 in. = 5 lb.

The general rule for determining the resultant (R) of a linear force system is that the resultant is equal to the algebraic sum of the forces acting, or

$$R = \Sigma F$$

(Σ, the Greek capital letter Sigma, indicates "the sum of.")

In the previous problem:

$$R = \Sigma F$$
$$= 15 + 15 + 15 - 2\frac{1}{2}$$
$$= 42\frac{1}{2} \text{ lb.}$$

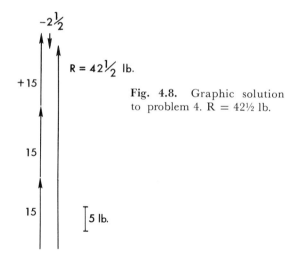

Fig. 4.8. Graphic solution to problem 4. R = 42½ lb.

5. Problem

A patient is exercising his shoulder extensor muscles with wall pulleys (Fig. 4.9). Weights of 20 lb., 10 lb., and 5 lb. are loaded on the weight pan, which itself weighs 4 lb. The patient is exerting an opposing force of 45 lb.

QUESTION. What is the resultant of the entire system of forces which is acting? Is the arm flexing, extending, or remaining stationary?

SOLUTION. (1) *Algebraic.* We will give the

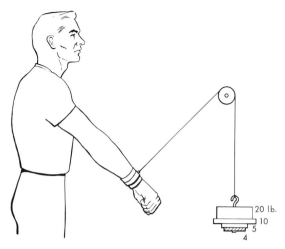

Fig. 4.9. Resistance exercise for shoulder extensor muscles, problem 5.

exercise weights a negative value and the force at the other end of the rope a positive value.

$$R = \Sigma F$$
$$= (-20) + (-10) + (-5) + (-4) + 45$$
$$= 6 \text{ lb. (in a positive direction)}$$

The weights are moving upward so the arm must be extending. The patient is overcoming the pull of the weights.

(2) *Graphic.* Figure 4.10; Scale 1 in. = 5 lb.

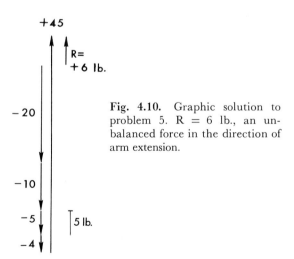

Fig. 4.10. Graphic solution to problem 5. R = 6 lb., an unbalanced force in the direction of arm extension.

The Equilibrium Problem

Whenever an unbalanced resultant force is applied to an object, as in problem 5 above, motion must take place. However, if the sum of the negative forces equals the sum of the positive forces the resultant is zero and no motion will take place. Here we have a condition of equilibrium.*

When we deal with force problems in which the object involved is known to be at rest, this is termed an *equilibrium problem.* The sum of the forces must equal zero:

$$\Sigma F = 0$$

6. Problem

A patient is seated on the edge of a plinth with his legs hanging vertically over the side (Fig. 4.11). A deLorme boot and bar weighing 2½ lb. are on one foot; to these are added weights of 10 lb., 15 lb., and 5 lb.

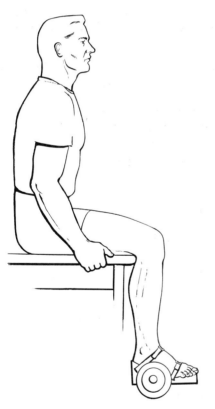

Fig. 4.11.   Exercise load at beginning of quadriceps exercise, problem 6.

QUESTION.   What is the total external load placed on the knee joint structures which support the leg in this position?

SOLUTION.   (1) *Algebraic.* According to Newton's third law, the knee structures must supply an "equal and opposite reaction" or opposing force to the externally applied load. If we give this upward tension or reaction force (T) a negative sign, and the added exercise loads a positive sign, we have:

$$\Sigma F = 0$$
$$2\tfrac{1}{2} + 10 + 15 + 5 - T = 0$$
$$32\tfrac{1}{2} - T = 0$$
$$T = 32\tfrac{1}{2} \text{ lb.}$$

(2) *Graphic.* Figure 4.12; scale 1 in. = 10 lb.

Note that the forces must form a closed figure; that is, the end of the last force must reach the beginning of the first. Note also that T is equal to the magnitude of the resultant of the applied forces but opposite in direction.

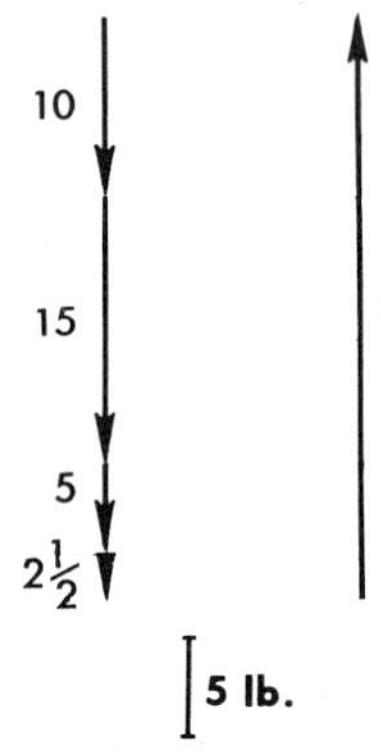

Fig. 4.12.   Graphic solution to problem 6. According to the scale 1 in. = 10 lb., the combined vector lengths equal 3¼ in., which represents 32½ lb.

Defining the equilibrium condition is one of the principal problems in statics. When it is known that the body involved is at rest or in a state of uniform motion, and some of the forces that are acting are known, the problem is to find the remaining unknown force or forces.

We have seen that, algebraically, the resultant of a linear force system is equal to the algebraic sum of the forces $(R = \Sigma F)$. For the resultant to be zero we must have the sum of the forces equal to zero $(\Sigma F = 0)$. In finding the resultant it was helpful to draw a picture or figure that showed all the forces that were acting on the body. Then these forces could be inserted into an equation or they could be used graphically to determine the resultant force.

Free body diagram.   In the equilibrium problem it is again desirable to have a figure that shows all of the forces that are acting. However, in this case some of the forces will be

* A body moving at uniform speed is also said to be in a condition of equilibrium, since there are no unbalanced forces.

unknown in magnitude and possibly also in direction. The first step is to draw the figure and place all the known forces on it in their proper locations. Then we determine where an unknown force might be acting on the figure. To aid us here we use Newton's third law which says that for every action there must be an equal and opposite reaction. If an object is touching our figure at a certain point, and we remove this object, we must place a force at the point of contact to give us the same effect as the object had at that point, since a force is defined as the action of one body on another, producing either a push or pull. Such a figure of a body that shows all the forces that are acting on it, whether they are known or unknown, is called a *free body diagram* (Fig. 4.13, 4.14).

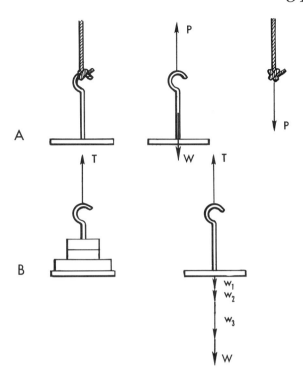

Fig. 4.14. A. A weight pan is suspended on a rope. To consider the forces acting on the pan, we draw it as a free body, replacing the rope by a vector, P. To consider forces acting in the rope, the weight pan is replaced by vector P.

B. Weights and weight pan are shown with opposing force T, and finally, rope and weight forces, T and w_1, w_2, w_3 acting on the weight pan, as well as gravitational pull on the pan itself, w. Arrangement of the free body diagram will depend on the nature of the problem.

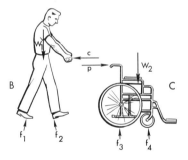

Fig. 4.13. A. An aide pushes a wheel chair across the floor.

B. Free body diagram of the aide, showing forces of the chair, C, and floor (f_1, f_2) as vectors.

C. Free body diagram of the chair, with forces of the man, P, and floor (f_3, f_4) shown as vectors.

Since we do not know the magnitude of the forces that exist between several bodies in contact, and since in some cases we don't know whether they exert a pull or a push on the body under consideration, it becomes necessary to introduce a vector to represent the force. Here we must assume a direction of the force. This assumed direction may be incorrect, but our solution will give us the correct direction according to the sign obtained in the algebraic solution of the problem. That is, if the answer is positive, the assumed direction was correct; if negative, the assumed direction was incorrect. For example,

7. Problem

A leg in a plaster cast is suspended in a sling by an overhead pulley and weight pan apparatus (Fig. 4.15A). The leg exerts a downward force of 35 lb. on the sling and the cast exerts an additional 11 lb. load at this point. Weights of 10, 10, and 30 lb. on the weight pan are supported by the pulley rope.

QUESTIONS. Will weight have to be removed or added to the weight pan in order to we have guessed incorrectly regarding its direction; this amount of weight must be removed from the weight pan rather than added to it if the system is in equilibrium.

(2) *Graphic.* Equilibrium requires that the forces in the vector diagram form a closed figure. That is, the beginning of the first vector and the end of the last vector must lie at the same point. This is true since the resultant equals the distance from the beginning of the first vector to the end of the last one, and if the resultant is to vanish, these two points must be coincident. We may now draw our vector diagram of all the forces, beginning with the known forces and drawing them in any order (Fig. 4.15C). Each force is properly laid off with regard to magnitude and direction, and after all the known forces are in place we have one force remaining which is the unknown force, P. It must be drawn so that its tip just reaches the beginning of the first vector. By measuring its length and knowing its location, we can determine both the magnitude and direction of this unknown force. As before, the graphic method serves as a check on the algebraic result.

The linear system of forces is an extremely simple one. About the only difficulty one is apt to have in the solution of problems is in giving an incorrect sign to a force to accompany its magnitude. However, it is important that a complete and clear understanding of the principles involved is obtained in dealing with this system, since other more complicated systems which we shall consider next are based on extensions of the principles made use of in the linear system.

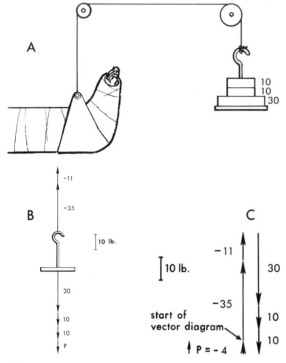

Fig. 4.15. A. Pulley weight suspension arrangement in problem 7. Upward forces are arbitrarily designated as negative; downward forces positive.
B. Free body diagram of weight pan. Estimated force P is added arbitrarily.
C. Graphic solution to problem 7. P = −0.4 inch, representing an upward force of 4 pounds.

just balance the load of the leg and cast in the sling? How much weight must be moved?

SOLUTION.   We draw a free body diagram of the weight pan and show all the forces that are acting on it (Fig. 4.15B). Instead of showing the weights, the leg, and the cast, we introduce as vectors the forces they exert on the pan. In order to provide for the adjustment of the weight, we will arbitrarily assume that we need additional downward pull on the rope to balance the leg. We must therefore place an arrow in the same direction as the original vectors and label the unknown force P.

(1) *Algebraic.* Since for equilibrium the sum of all the forces must be zero, we can write:

$$\Sigma F = 0$$
$$-35 - 11 + 30 + 10 + 10 + P = 0$$
$$P = -4 \text{ lb.}$$

The magnitude of the weight which must be moved is 4 lb. Since the result for P is negative,

(Solve the following problems by both the graphic and algebraic method for practice in diagraming.)

1. Assume your body weight to be 120 lb.; you are standing and holding a load of books weighing 12 lb. What is the total force between your feet and the ground? Between each foot and the ground? Is this tension or compression force?

2. Your forearm weighs 4 lb. and you are

carrying a portable diathermy machine weighing 24 lb. (Your elbow is extended.) What is the force in the joint structures and muscles crossing the elbow joint counterbalancing this load? Is this tension or compression force? What is the magnitude of the tension force at the shoulder?

3. A patient exercising on wall pulleys pulls on the rope with a force of 70 lb.; the load on the weights is also 70 lb. What force exists in the rope as a result of these forces that are applied to its ends? Is the arm moving?

4. A Sayre sling has a single supporting strand of rope to which is applied a force of 25 lb. What magnitude of tension is produced in the structures of the neck when traction is applied to a 200 lb. patient in a sitting position? What would the answer be if the sling were suspended by a pulley system with three supporting strands instead of one? (Ignore the weight of the apparatus.)

5. A patient weighing 135 lb. hangs by both hands from the top rung of the stall bars. What pressure is produced between each hand and the bar? What is this pressure if he stands on a scale and supports 30 lb. of his weight on his feet instead of hanging free?

6. A pole 6 feet high serving as a weight rack for storing exercise weights has five pegs along its length at 1 ft. intervals. Starting at the bottom the weights are 75 lb., 75 lb., 50 lb., 30 lb., with 15 lb. at the top. (a) What is the maximum total force at the bottom of the pole? (b) Find the compression force in the pole between the 50 and 30 lb. weights. (c) Compare the relative compression forces on the intervertebral disks at various levels of the vertebral column; the relative superincumbent weight supported by the ankle, knee, and hip joints in standing; and the tension forces in the shoulder, elbow, and wrist joint structures when the arm is hanging at the side.

7. A 180 lb. man has a walking cast on one leg which weighs 12 lb. What is the total tension in the joint structures crossing the hip joint and supporting this load and the limb when the foot is elevated off the floor? What is the total tension in the joint structures crossing the knee?

CHAPTER FIVE

Parallel Forces in One Plane

The next subject to be considered is the case where the action lines of the forces are all parallel to each other but not in a line. For example, when the forearm is flexed to horizontal, gravity pulls downward on the forearm and the biceps muscle pulls upward, but the action lines of these two forces do not coincide (Fig. 5.1). A weight in the hand adds still another parallel force to the system, and the force on the distal humerus may also be included in our problem. So we now must consider not only the magnitude and direction of the forces acting on the object but also their relative positions in the plane.

In the previous chapter we dealt with linear forces, which caused compression or tension effects. The arrangement of forces in a parallel manner usually provides a bending effect on the object. Since the human body is a system of linked segments, parallel forces often cause rotation of the parts about their anatomical axes. Both muscle and gravitational forces are extremely important in producing these turning effects which are fundamental in body movement. Innumerable examples of parallel forces acting on the body segments may be cited, as well as mechanical devices which are operated by parallel forces. A familiar example is a

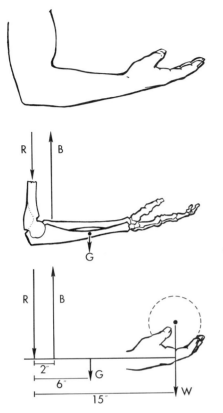

Fig. 5.1. A parallel force system acting on the fore-arm in which W = weight in the hand; G = gravitational pull on the forearm; B = upward force of biceps muscle; and R = reaction force, shown as pressure of humerus against ulna. (A pressure equal and opposite to R is applied by the ulna against the humerus).

child's teeter-totter (Fig. 5.2). This illustrates the importance of lever length in relation to the rotational effect of a force, as we shall see.

In approaching problems of parallel forces in a plane, we select a reference point and determine forces which act clockwise or counterclockwise about this point. We again have two types of basic problems—finding a resultant, and the equilibrium problem in which the object concerned is known to be at rest. The type of problem depends on the data at hand.

Resultants. Finding the resultant of a system of parallel forces in a plane is similar to obtaining the resultant in the linear system. As before, we add all the forces in one direction and subtract all the forces in the opposite direction, and the answer gives us the magnitude of the resultant force ($R = \Sigma F$). The sign of the answer gives us the direction of the resultant force. However, one very important difference exists

between the resultant of this system and the resultant of the linear system. In the linear system the action line of the resultant had to lie along the same line with the original forces, while in the case of parallel forces the position of the action line of the resultant is unknown. To locate the position of this action line we make use of a principle which has wide use throughout the entire field of mechanics. This is called the *principle of moments,* but before stating this principle we must define moment.

THE MOMENT OF A FORCE ABOUT ANY POINT IS EQUAL TO THE MAGNITUDE OF THE FORCE MULTIPLIED BY THE PERPENDICULAR DISTANCE FROM THE ACTION LINE OF THE FORCE TO THAT POINT.

This perpendicular distance from the force to the fulcrum or point selected is known as the lever arm (l) of the force. ("Torque" is another term used to designate a force times its lever arm.)

A moment, then, is the product of a *force* and a *distance* ($M = F \times l$). It gives us the turning effect of the force about the selected point. We can imagine a lever arm extending from the point in question—which now might be considered a fulcrum or bearing—to the action line of the force. The force then produces a turning effect of the lever about this point, and the effectiveness of the force in rotating the object depends on its distance from the fulcrum. When you turn a crank the total rotary effect depends not only on the amount of force you exert but also on the length of the crank.

In Figure 5.1 the turning effect, or moment, of the weight in the hand about the elbow is

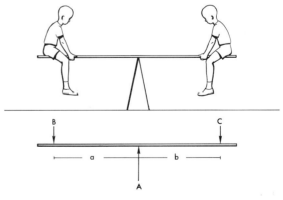

Fig. 5.2. B and C both produce rotational forces about axis A—B in a counterclockwise direction and C in a clockwise direction.

W × 15 inches; of gravitational pull on the forearm, G × 6 inches; and of the biceps muscle, B × 2 inches. Since the lever arms of W and G are larger than that of B, force B must be very large to counterbalance moments exerted by forces G and W.

Since a moment is a force times a distance, it may be increased or decreased in either of two ways—by changing the magnitude of the force or by changing its distance from the fulcrum. In the case of the teeter-totter the moment exerted by child "A" about the fulcrum is his weight times the distance he sits from the fulcrum. He can change this moment or turning effect by moving up or back on the board but he cannot alter his weight (Fig. 5.3). In the case of the biceps supporting the forearm at 90 degrees of elbow flexion, the lever arm may be considered as the perpendicular distance from the tendon to the axis of the elbow joint. In this instance the lever arm is (anatomically) fixed, but the magnitude of the muscle force can be varied to alter the moment.

The clockwise (CW) or counterclockwise (CCW) rotation of forces about the selected bearing point is indicated by means of a positive or negative sign (Fig. 5.4). Or we can des-

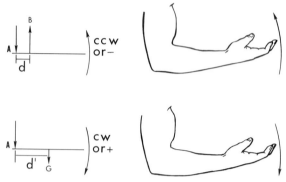

Fig. 5.4. Designation of clockwise, CW, and counterclockwise, CCW, turning forces. The choice of signs to denote these is arbitrary but once selected must be used consistently throughout the problem. B × d = moment of biceps pull; G × d' = moment of gravitational force. Force at joint = A.

ignate the actual direction of rotation by small curved arrows. In the example shown, the biceps pull is a counterclockwise force opposed by the clockwise force of gravity, both acting about a bearing point or fulcrum at the elbow joint. These two opposing forces acting on the forearm follow exactly the same rule in regard to moments as do the two children on the teeter-totter, even though here they are both on the same side of the fulcrum. When the forearm is in equilibrium, B × d must equal G × d'.

Let us consider some further examples. If two boys of equal weight are to balance one another on a teeter-totter, they must sit the same distance from the fulcrum of the board. If one boy plays with his smaller brother who is half his weight, the brother must sit twice as far from the fulcrum in order to balance. If the brother weighed one-third as much he would have to sit three times as far back, and so on. The clockwise force times its lever arm must equal the counterclockwise force times its lever arm (Fig. 5.5).

In the example of the biceps muscle supporting the forearm (Fig. 5.6), suppose the forearm weighs 5 pounds and its center of gravity is 6 inches from the elbow joint. The biceps has a lever arm of 2 inches, let us say, and the muscle must therefore pull with a force of 15 pounds in order for the clockwise moment to equal the counterclockwise moment.

Since a moment or torque is the product of a force and a distance, the units of moments are given in inch-pounds, foot-pounds, kilogram-

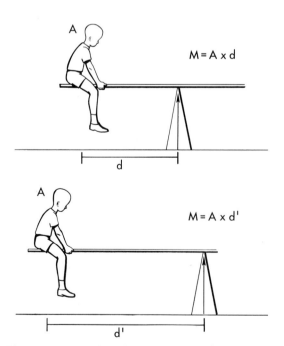

Fig. 5.3. When the child moves away from the axis, the body weight is not altered but its turning effect (moment, M) about the axis is increased since its lever arm becomes longer: A × d' > A × d.

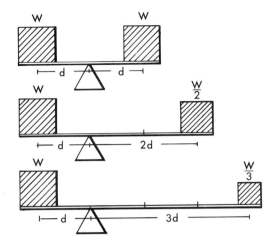

Fig. 5.5. Ratio of distance to weights for a given moment value. Here as the weight is decreased its lever arm is proportionately increased to maintain balance.

centimeters, or whatever units of measurement of distance and force are being used.

The concept of the moment of a force has such important kinesiological and clinical applications that it might be well to consider some further examples of this principle in relation to single forces before going on with an analysis of force systems. The following section will be devoted to illustrations of moments and their application. A few review questions will follow, to help the student test his understanding of the material.

In body movement we deal with two basic sets of forces: (1) *gravitational* forces, which give the body stability, and (2) *muscular* forces, which interact with and oppose gravity to maintain the upright posture and to produce body movements such as ambulation and manipulation of objects.

In the case of *moments of gravitational forces,* one element only can be altered—the lever length. The mass of the body or of a segment, like the weight of the boy on the teeter-totter, does not change. However, the *effectiveness* of this weight for rotation can be changed by shifting its position in relation to the fulcrum, or turning point. The action line of the gravitational force on a part can be moved nearer to or farther from the axis of the joint by changing the position of the part in space. For example, an exercise involving leg raising can be performed with the knee straight or with it flexed (Fig. 5.7). The moment of the gravitational force is greater with the knee straight, not because the force (segment weight) has changed, but because the distance from the action line of the gravitational force to the hip axis has changed. This principle is used constantly in therapeutic exercises to vary the exercise load.

In the case of *moments of muscle force* both the magnitude of the force and its lever arm may change as the body segment is moved. However,

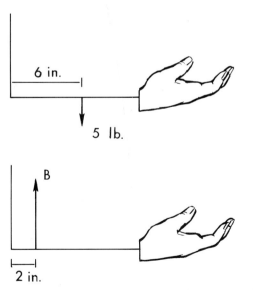

Fig. 5.6. Computation of moments of forearm weight (5 lb.) and biceps, B, support: $6 \times 5 = B \times 2$; $B = 15$ lb. The moments of gravitational force and of biceps pull are each 30 inch-pounds.

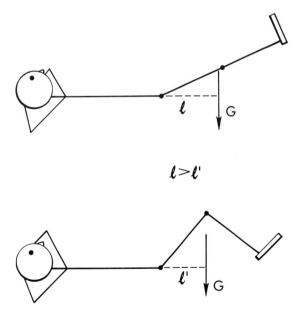

Fig. 5.7. The moment of gravitational force, G, on the lower limb, exerting a clockwise turning effect about the hip, is decreased by flexing the knees: $l > l'$.

the shift in lever arm is restricted to a rigid path by anatomical limitations. For example, when the elbow is straight the lever arm of the biceps muscle is short. The lever arm increases as the elbow bends, is maximal at about 90 degrees of flexion, and again decreases beyond this point (Fig. 5.8) On the other hand, the magnitude of the muscle force can be voluntarily altered at any point in the range of motion. In normal persons, the strength of muscle contraction is precisely graded and controlled by central nervous system mechanisms so that it is appropriate to the activity performed. The moments produced result from finely graded muscle forces interacting with, and compensating for, the fixed pattern of change in lever arm of the muscles.

A full discussion of segmental forces in body movement should include not only biomechanical but also physiological considerations of muscle length-tension relationships and controlling neuromotor mechanisms. Sensory feedback apparatus is a most important factor in adequate neuromuscular function. However, in this text we are concerned only with the mechanical aspects and will simply note in passing that this is not the whole story.

Further illustrations of the principle of moments are grouped as follows:

1. Internally applied forces, including anatomical arrangements of muscles and tendons in relation to the joints they control

2. Externally applied forces, including (a) gravitational pull on the body and body parts, (b) manual and mechanical resistances in therapeutic exercises and stretching procedures, and (c) forces applied to the body by prostheses and in the use of tools and implements.

Internally Applied Forces. When anatomical arrangements of muscles in relation to joint movement are analyzed, it is customary to place the arbitrary turning point about which moments are taken at the anatomical axis of the joint. When this is done the moment of the joint reactive force is zero since its action line passes through this point. A theoretical set of axes and planes, such as that utilized by Adolph Fick, can then be visualized, with the origin of the system at the anatomical joint. (The anatomical joint axis frequently shifts during movement, but we can approximate its location for our purposes.) The action line of a muscle producing motion about a joint is determined by its anatomical position; its lever arm is the perpendicular distance from the action line of the muscle or tendon to the axis of rotation of the joint. From the definition of a moment we know that the farther a tendon lies from the axis of

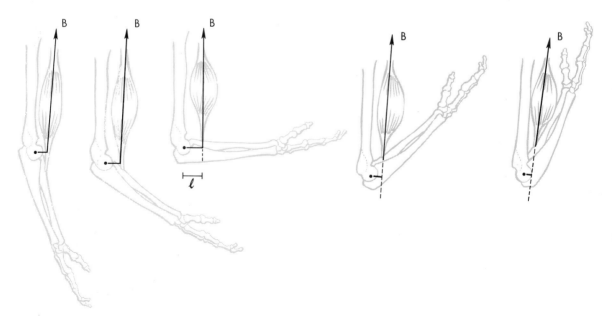

Fig. 5.8.   The biceps, B, at various points of elbow flexion, showing variations in the lever arm (perpendicular distance from action line of tendon to elbow axis).

the joint the better will be its turning effect on the segment about the joint—the better its crank handle, so to say.

1. The interposition of the patella between the tendon of the quadriceps (Q) and the femur increases the lever arm of the knee extensor muscle force (Fig. 5.9). Surgical removal of this bone (patellectomy) results in a decreased lever arm and hence a decreased moment of the quadriceps pull in knee extension. This may be compensated for by exercises designed to strengthen the quadriceps muscle.

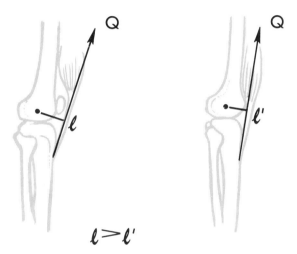

Fig. 5.9. The patella increases the lever arm of the quadriceps force, Q, at the knee.

2. Figure 5.10 shows how the rotatory effect of the hip abductor muscles (A) on the pelvis, preventing it from dropping on the unsupported side during walking, is enhanced by the normal angulation of the neck of the femur on the shaft (125 to 130 degrees in adults). In conditions in which the angle between the femoral neck and shaft is increased or the neck is shortened, this advantageous lever arm of the muscles is shortened and the moment of the muscle force thereby decreased. Again, increased muscle force must be made available to compensate.

3. The tendon of Achilles is placed on the posterior aspect of the calcaneus as far as possible from the ankle joint, giving the muscles the maximum possible advantage in rotating the foot (Fig. 5.11). (The triceps tendon at the elbow joint is attached on the tip of the olecranon process in a similar fashion.) With plantar flexion the lever arm of the gastrocnemius-

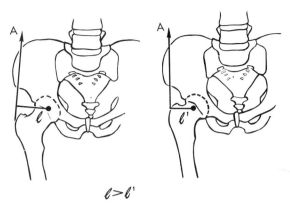

Fig. 5.10. Normal and abnormal lever arms of the hip abductor muscles, A. Shortening and change in angulation of the femoral neck in the diagram on the right modifies the lever length of the muscle.

soleus is shortened slightly, while in dorsiflexion it is slightly lengthened. However, it changes very little.

4. Steindler has suggested an operation for increasing the elbow flexor strength in paralytic patients. The forearm flexor group is transferred surgically to a point higher on the humerus, thus increasing the lever arm of these muscles in elbow flexion. This procedure also improves the muscle length and ability to exert tension in the physiological sense.

Externally Applied Forces. *Moments of Gravitational Forces.* Just as we think of a muscle pulling at its anatomical attachment on a segment, we can think of the force of gravity exerting a downward pull at the center of gravity of the body parts. Gravity cannot be

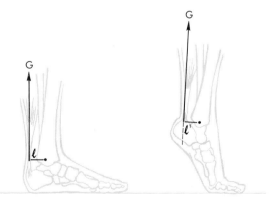

Fig. 5.11. The lever arm of the Achilles tendon force, G, changes only slightly in foot movements. Compare this lever arm with that of such plantar flexor muscles as peroneus longus and brevis, flexor hallucis longus, and tibialis posterior.

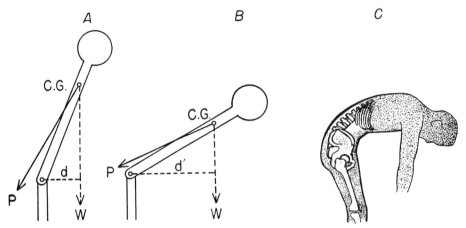

Fig. 5.12. Comparative moment of gravitational pull on the trunk in two positions of trunk flexion: d' > d. (Strait et al.[1])

seen, as we can see muscles and tendons, but its effect is just as real. Since the center of gravity moves in space as the part moves, the lever arm of gravitational pull (perpendicular distance from the action line of gravitational force to the axis at the joint) changes according to the position of the part (Fig. 2.20). Analysis of posture and movement is based on an understanding of the leverage afforded gravitational force by body position. A segment is more difficult to lift when it is fully extended than when it is flexed. This knowledge not only enables us to grade exercises effectively but to minimize gravitational effects in every-day activity. Everyone, and physical therapists particularly, should know how to conserve energy and to prevent strain and injury to joint structures. Low back injury commonly results from ignorance of safe lifting techniques which minimize gravitational effects. Arm and shoulder strain may result from prolonged use of the hands away from the midline of the body.

Examples

1. Strait, Inman, and Ralston[1] have demonstrated the tremendous low back strain involved in forward trunk flexion. According to their calculations, the compressive force in the fifth lumbar vertebra of a 180 lb. man with his trunk flexed 60 degrees from vertical, arms hanging freely, is 450 lb. If he holds a 50 lb. weight in his hands the compression force on the fifth lumbar vertebra is nearly 850 lb. In Figure 5.12, the lumbosacral joint is considered to be a fixed fulcrum; P represents the spinal

extensor muscle force necessary to counter-balance W, the weight of the head, arms and trunk, acting at the center of gravity in the thorax; d increases as the trunk is flexed and hence the moment of the gravity force increases even though W does not change in magnitude. Thus P must become very large, resulting in dangerous compression of the lumbar intervertebral disks.*

2. Stooping by flexing the trunk forward likewise gives gravitational force a fine lever arm with which to put strain on the low back structures, as does reaching by bending at the waist. Making beds is a daily chore which can easily lead to back injury if not done properly. Work involving use of the arms, such as carrying trays, typing, or peeling vegetables, should be done with the elbows close to the sides to minimize strain on supporting muscles.

3. Shifting the mass of body weight is used in many ways in grading therapeutic exercises. A good example is the "sit-up" exercise which is most easily performed with the arms at the sides (Fig. 5.13). Steps of increasing difficulty consist of moving the arms to various positions higher on the trunk (arms across the abdomen, over the chest, on the opposite shoulders). Most difficult is sitting up with the arms extended overhead, since here the center of gravity of the trunk and arms is farthest from the axis at the hip joints.

---

*It has been determined that part of the force due to bending is carried by the body wall which acts as a stressed skin structure caused by internal pressure. Compare the resistance to bending of a long balloon.

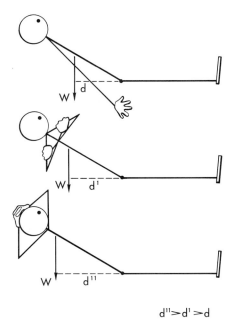

Fig. 5.13. The lever arm of gravitational force, W, on the trunk is increased by moving the arms upward (lever arm $d'' > d' > d$).

4. The classic abdominal muscle strengthening exercise of flexing one knee toward the chest, straightening it toward the ceiling, and lowering the extended limb to the table demonstrates several stages of difficulty (Fig. 5.14). The action line of the gravitational force of the limb approaches the hip axis as the part is raised, passes through the joint during knee extension, and then moves away from the axis as the limb is lowered ($d'' > d' > d$). This final phase requires increasing effort of the abdominal muscles to stabilize the pelvis and prevent lordosis caused by tension of the iliopsoas and the other hip flexors pulling on their proximal attachments. Many patients must first lower the limb with the knee flexed and progress to lowering with full knee extension later on.

5. Various arm positions are used in exercises to strengthen back and shoulder muscles. Lifting the flexed arms requires less effort than lifting them extended. Of course, there are other factors to consider in evaluating the difficulty of specific exercises, such as the length of the antagonist muscles and the relative size of the various body segments of the patient.

In analyzing gravitational forces in body movement, remember that the downward pull on the body is opposed by an equal upward push of the supporting surface, whether one is in a recumbent, sitting, or a standing position. Frictional forces must be sufficient to stabilize the body. Adequate floor reactions are necessary, particularly for walking or running to be successful. The many joints of the body which support segments above them sustain compression forces. Both the superincumbent part and the supporting member on which it rests must resist equal and opposite forces applied to their respective articular surfaces. The shape of the joints and the arrangement of reinforcing ligaments and tendons are such that the upright posture is maintained with an economy of neuromuscular effort.

Another important aspect of gravitational force acting on the body is the effect which counter pressure of supporting surfaces has on neuromuscular mechanisms controlling posture and directing movement. For example, pressure on the soles of the feet activates the positive support reaction. Both exteroceptive and proprioceptive stimuli from skin, muscles, and joint structures contribute to the barrage of afferent impulses by which the central nervous system is able to maintain the delicate synergies of balance and movement. The vast importance of

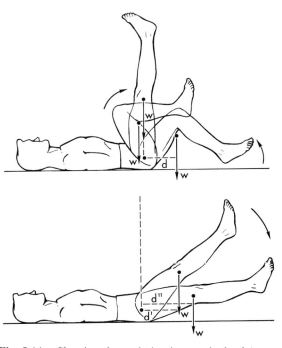

Fig. 5.14. Showing the variation in exercise load (moment of lower limb, W × d) with different phases of a posture exercise. W = gravitational pull acting at the center of gravity of the limb; d = distance of action line to the hip axis; $d'' > d' > d$ (see text).

these mechanical and neurological interactions is coming to be more fully appreciated in analysis of motor learning and body movements.

Manual and Mechanical. Here a third category of forces is added to the muscular and gravitational forces. External forces applied by manual and mechanical means are used in physical therapy procedures such as manual muscle testing, assistive and resistive exercises, and stretching and mobilization of joint structures. In manually applied forces all characteristics defining the force can be controlled—magnitude, action line and direction, and point of application on the body. In most situations the lever arm of the force applied is made as long as possible; that is, force is applied to the distal end of the segment to obtain maximum effect.

1. In muscle testing, manual resistance is usually applied at the far end of the segment involved, just proximal to the next distal joint. This gives the applied force a much better lever arm than that of the muscles being tested (Fig. 5.15).

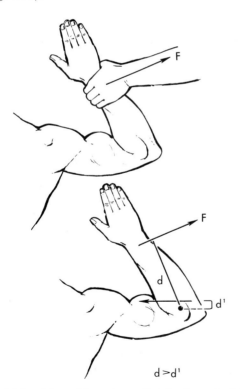

Fig. 5.15. Manual force is applied far from the joint in muscle testing in order to obtain maximal rotational effect: F × d = moment. The lever arm of an elbow flexor muscle such as the brachialis is shown as d′, which illustrates the relative disadvantage in turning effect of the muscles being tested.

2. Manual resistance exercises usually follow the same rule, with the therapist's hand a maximum distance from the axis of joint rotation—at the end of the segment. In this situation the patient must work hard to overcome relatively slight externally applied force. Manual assistance to movement may be given in a similar fashion, with a long lever arm.

In some instances the therapist purposely shortens the lever arm of the applied force, usually in order to obtain better control of the pressure. For example, in the manual muscle test for hip adduction, the examiner's hand might be placed at the ankle to obtain a maximum test force moment (Fig. 5.16). However,

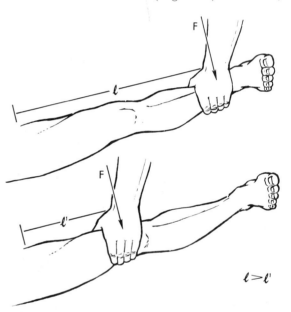

Fig. 5.16. Two possible manual muscle test positions for hip adductors, with long and short lever arms (*l* and *l′*) for manual force, F.

manual pressure is usually given above the knee because it is easier to direct and grade the force opposing the adductors, and the therapist can more satisfactorily control the patient's position on the table and stabilize the pelvis with his other hand. By pressing at the knee he is required to push twice as hard as he would at the ankle to obtain the same test force effectiveness (moment).

3. When manual force is applied in muscle stretching procedures the hand may grasp the segment close to the joint involved (Fig. 5.17). Here again, an effective lever arm for the applied force is sacrificed in order to obtain bet-

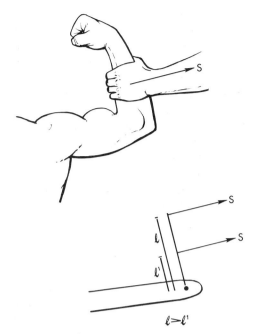

Fig. 5.17. A short lever arm in applying manual pressure, S, sacrifices force for control. The moment of the force would be greater if it were applied at the wrist. $(S \times l > S \times l')$.

ter control of the movement. Also, the moment afforded the external force by a maximum lever arm might be sufficient to injure the joint structures; a shorter lever arm is safer.

Exercise resistance and assistance supplied by mechanical means also is usually applied to the body by placing a sling or cuff at the end of the

segment involved. In various pulley devices, Elgin table exercise arrangements, deLorme boot for quadriceps strengthening, and countless other devices, the full length of the body segment is utilized in applying the external force. The external force therefore is maximally effective and has a much better lever arm than the opposing muscles.

The concept of moments may be utilized in the design and operation of mechanical devices of the type just mentioned. An example is Storms' exercise apparatus for quadriceps strengthening.[2] A wooden beam is attached to the floor by a hinge at one end (Fig. 5.18). A series of pegs is provided along which weights may be hung at various distances from the hinge or fulcrum. To increase difficulty the weights may be applied farther from the fulcrum. The subject swings the beam upward by means of a cord attached at either end to the beam. The cord passes through a loop fastened to the patient's foot. As the knee is extended, the force applied to the leg decreases because: (1) the lever length of the lifting force increases (distance from the loop at the foot to the hinge); and (2) the lever arm of gravitational force pulling on the beam decreases as the beam moves from horizontal toward vertical. Thus with this apparatus the resistance applied to the quadriceps decreases toward the end of its range of motion at full knee extension as the muscle's ability to exert tension declines. Storms

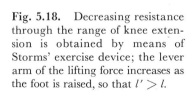

Fig. 5.18. Decreasing resistance through the range of knee extension is obtained by means of Storms' exercise device; the lever arm of the lifting force increases as the foot is raised, so that $l' > l$.

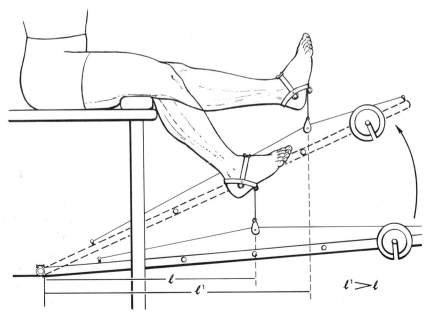

pointed out that this pattern of resistance applied to the quadriceps is parallel to the normal functional load on the muscle in body movement.

Exercise resistances applied to the patient by means of mechanical devices can be measured and therefore repeated exactly, and these methods conserve the energy of the therapist. However, the resistance offered by these devices follows a fixed path with a predestined variation in force, whether applied by pulley weight or by a lever device. Thus this method of exercise assistance or resistance cannot approach the flexibility in application of manually applied force which can be varied in magnitude and direction as required. In the muscle re-education of many types of patients there is no substitute for the skill of an experienced physical therapist working directly with the patient and gauging his needs from moment to moment.

Still another clinical area of application of external forces in body movement is in the use of canes and crutches. Here ground reaction forces are applied to the trunk in walking not only through the lower limbs but also through the assistive device (Fig. 5.19). Some degree of elbow flexion is common when a cane is used. The upward thrust of the cane with weight-bearing tends to flex the elbow joint and to elevate and extend the shoulder, requiring strong

stabilizing activity of the triceps, latissimus dorsi, and pectoral muscles particularly. The greater the flexion of the elbow, the greater are the moments around the elbow and shoulder resulting from ground reaction forces. The same principle applies to the use of crutches where the weight is borne on the hands.

When the cane is used, "locking" the elbow in full extension spares the triceps muscle, just as keeping the knee straight in walking spares the quadriceps. Canadian crutches, with a posterior band around the forearm, help to oppose elbow flexion. The upright is angled in such a way that downward pressure on the hand bar pushes the forearm cuff forward, forcing the elbow into extension.

An abnormal gait commonly seen is explained by the concept of moments. Normally when one foot is lifted from the floor, the center of gravity of the supported body weight resting on the stance hip lies medial to the head of the femur (G, Fig. 5.20). This mass includes the head, arms,

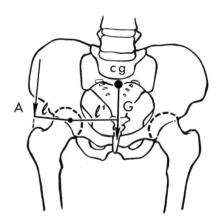

Fig. 5.20. Static forces acting about the femoral head in the frontal plane in unilateral stance: G = weight of the body acting medial to the hip axis in a clockwise direction; A = force of the abductor muscles acting counterclockwise to stabilize the pelvis. The head of the femur must support G + A. (Note similarity to Fig. 5.2). Here $G \times l' = A \times l$.

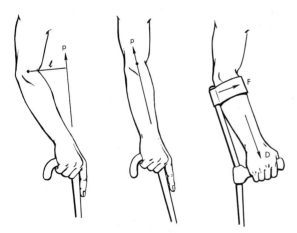

Fig. 5.19. Moments related to use of a cane. As the hand pushes downward, the elbow is forced into flexion and the shoulder tends to extend. The moment about the elbow axis is $P \times l$. If the elbow is fully extended, the torque is reduced, or absent if the lever arm becomes zero. Pressure, D, downward against the handrest of Canadian crutches provides force, F, forward against the forearm to stabilize the elbow joint and to prevent elbow flexion.

trunk and opposite limb, which tend by their weight to force the pelvis to drop downward on the unsupported side. This drop is normally controlled by the hip abductor muscles on the stance side which contract to stabilize the pelvis in the frontal plane. These two forces are opposed by the upward reacting force of the femoral head. Note in Figure 5.20 the similarity to the two boys on the teeter-totter in Figures 5.2 and 5.3. Remember that as one boy moved inward toward the fulcrum, the effectiveness of his body weight as a turning force decreased. Likewise, if a patient has weak hip abductor muscles he leans his trunk *toward* the affected hip and walks with a so-called "abductor" gait (Fig. 5.21). Leaning the trunk sideways toward the affected hip moves the center of gravity of the supported weight closer to the fulcrum at the femoral head, reducing the moment of the body weight about the stance hip, and consequently reducing the need for the hip abductor muscles to stabilize the pelvis. In the case of flail abductor muscles, the patient may shift the trunk so far to the side that the line of gravity falls lateral to the hip joint, stabilizing the joint in the frontal plane.

At first it may seem strange that the femoral head in walking must push upward with a force greater than the weight of the segments it supports. Figure 5.20 shows that this weight (G), acting at a considerable distance medial to the hip axis, must be counterbalanced by a downward force (A), acting on the lateral side of the joint with a relatively smaller lever arm.

Inman[3] has estimated the forces G and A and their respective lever arms to be such that the static compression force on the head of the femur is 2.4 to 2.6 times the body weight in unilateral stance. Balancing the superincumbent weight over the head of the femur reduces this pressure to body weight alone (minus the mass of the supporting limb). For this reason persons with painful hip joints, as well as those with paralyzed hip abductor muscles, lean sharply toward the affected side as they walk. This is often referred to as a "gluteus medius" limp, a term which ignores other important hip abductor muscles which also act to stabilize the pelvis in the frontal plane (gluteus minimus, tensor fasciae latae, upper fibers of gluteus maximus inserting into the iliotibial band).

Blount[4] has pointed out the effectiveness of the lever arm of a cane carried in the contralateral hand in supporting the pelvis in the frontal plane (Fig. 5.22). The distance from the hip axis to the cane is vastly greater than the distance from the hip to the action line of the adjacent abductor muscles which normally prevent the pelvis from dropping downward on the unsupported side. Blount estimates that leaning with a pressure of 38 lb. on a cane held in the opposite hand will reduce the superincumbent

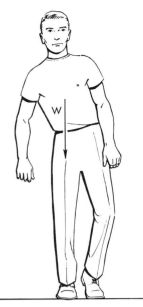

Fig. 5.21. Method of walking when hip abductors are weak. The patient shifts his weight, W, over the supporting femoral head, *toward* the affected side.

pressure on the femoral head from 385 lb. to 66 lb. in an "average" person. (Note that Blount's and Inman's figures compare favorably; if the superincumbent pressure on the femoral head is 2.5 times body weight, and $2.5X = 385$, then X, or body weight, would be 154 lb.)

A cane held in the hand on the same side as the involved hip has a much less favorable lever arm, so that considerably more pressure on the hand would be required to relieve hip pressure to the same degree as if the cane were held on the opposite side.

Fig. 5.22. Correction of abductor gait with cane held in the opposite hand. The supporting force, C, is applied through a favorable lever arm.

Countless additional examples of force applications involving the concept of moments could be given. Kinesiologists commonly differentiate between two basic types of motion: (1) *rotatory*, in which the object or body rotates about a turning point or axis, and (2) *translatory*, in which an object moves without rotation, as an ice boat glides or a boy slides down a banister. Since the body segments are articulated by series of anatomical joints, rotary movements of the segments form the basis of nearly all skeletal activity. Thus rotational forces, both external and internal, which act on the segments are of tremendous importance, and an understanding of the concept of moments is clearly essential to analysis of human movement.

Questions

(In answering some of the following, reference to a mounted skeleton will be helpful.)

1. How does the lever arm of the brachialis muscle vary through the range of elbow flexion as compared with the variation in lever arm of the triceps in elbow extension? (Do they vary equally?)

2. Is there more variation in lever length of the hamstrings during knee flexion than of the tendo-Achilles during plantar flexion? At which joint positions are these lever arms maximal? Minimal?

3. For the following, visualize and estimate the lever arm and its variation through the range of motion:

    (a) the semimembranosus in hip extension, knee flexion

    (b) the gluteus medius in hip abduction

    (c) the wrist and ankle flexors

    (d) other muscles and movements

4. A 60 lb. boy, A, sits 5 ft. from the axis of a teeter-totter facing a 50 lb. boy, B, on the other end of the board. How far from the axis must B sit to balance A? Where would B have to sit if A weighed 40 lb.?

5. Let us say your own elbow is flexed to 90 degrees with the forearm horizontal. Estimate the weight of the forearm and hand and the distance from its center of gravity to the elbow axis (refer to Fig. 2.3, p. 10).

    (a) What is the moment of the gravitational force tending to extend the forearm?

    (b) If the biceps tendon is 2 in. from the elbow axis, what force must this muscle exert to maintain the forearm in a horizontal position?

6. Give an example of a muscle that pulls at an angle of 90 degrees to the long axis of the part at some point in the range of motion. Are there many such muscles? Give an example of a muscle force in which the lever arm has little variation through the range of joint motion.

7. When you stand at the end of a diving board 10 ft. from where it is anchored to the ground, what moment do you exert about the fixed point of the board? Where would a person 1¼ times your weight stand in order to exert the same moment about this fixed point?

8. Why is it more difficult to do a sit-up exercise with the arms above the head than with them at the side of the trunk (diagram)?

9. A shoulder wheel has a handle which may be adjusted at various distances from the center or axis. Compare the effort required by the patient to turn the wheel when the handle is 6 in. and when it is 15 in. from the center point.

10. From the point of view of resistance offered by the weight of the limb, is it easier when lying supine to perform a "leg raising exercise" with the knee extended than with it flexed? Why?

11. At what point during a "leg raising exercise" (subject supine) is lumbar hyperextension most likely to occur? Why?

Resultants: Center of Gravity Determinations

Let us return now to the matter of finding the resultant of a force system, or series of parallel forces. For this purpose the principle of moments is stated as follows:

THE MOMENT OF THE RESULTANT FORCE ABOUT ANY ARBITRARILY SELECTED POINT MUST BE EQUAL BOTH IN MAGNITUDE AND DIRECTION TO THE ALGEBRAIC SUM OF THE MOMENTS OF THE INDIVIDUAL FORCES OF THE SYSTEM ABOUT THE SAME POINT.

Let an example illustrate how this principle permits us to locate the position of the action line of the resultant of the parallel force system. (Only algebraic solutions to these problems will be considered at this time. The graphic solution appears at the end of the next chapter, p. 87).

1. Problem

Consider three parallel forces acting vertically downward whose magnitudes from left to right are 32, 12, and 24 lb. The distance between the 32 and 12 lb. forces is 12 in., and the distance between the 12 and 24 lb. forces is 7 in. (Fig. 5.23A).

QUESTION. Find the resultant of the three forces—the single force which would have the same effect as all three.

SOLUTION. As in the linear system, the magnitude of the resultant is equal to the sum of the forces ($R = \Sigma F$). Thus,

$$R = 32 + 12 + 24$$
$$= 68 \text{ lb.}$$

We now know the magnitude of the resultant. In this problem all the forces are acting in the same direction so the resultant also must be acting in that direction, which in this case is downward. The remaining unknown term is the location of the resultant. We must apply the principle of moments to determine its position, and the first step is to choose a point from which to compute moments.

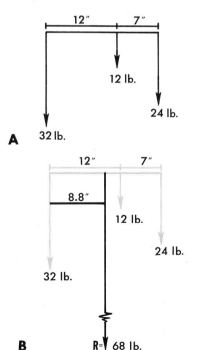

A 32 lb.

B R= 68 lb.

Fig. 5.23. A. Diagram of force system, problem 1.
B. Location and magnitude of resultant, problem 1.

It is desirable to select the point to be used as the moment center or fulcrum on the action line of one of the forces. This eliminates one term from the equation since the distance from that force to the selected point is zero. Selecting a moment center on the action line of the 32 lb. force, we will designate as X the distance from this point to the action line of the resultant, R. Then, according to the law of moments, R times X must be equal to the sum of the moments of the original forces about the moment center, and X will be equal to the sum of those moments divided by R, the magnitude of the resultant (Fig. 5.23B).

$$RX = \Sigma M$$
$$RX = (12 \times 12) + (24 \times 19)$$
$$= 144 + 456$$
$$= 600 \text{ in.-lb.}$$

We have already determined that $R = 68$ lb.; hence

$$68X = 600$$
$$X = \frac{600}{68}$$
$$X = 8.8 \text{ in.}$$

Since the two original forces both tend to rotate in a clockwise direction about the chosen moment center, the resultant force must also tend to rotate in the clockwise direction. The resultant is acting downward so the X distance, 8.8 in., must be measured to the right of the moment center in order to locate the action line of the resultant properly (i.e., a downward force rotating clockwise).

2. Problem

To illustrate that the center about which moments are taken can be selected arbitrarily at any point, let us repeat the computation, taking the action line of the 24 lb. force as the moment center (Fig. 5.24).

$$RX = \Sigma M$$
$$68X = (32 \times 19) + (12 \times 7)$$
$$X = \frac{608 + 84}{68}$$
$$X = 10.2 \text{ in.}$$

Here the forces are acting in a counterclockwise direction about the selected moment center; therefore, the resultant must be located 10.2 inches to the left of this point, or at precisely the location arrived at in the previous solution.

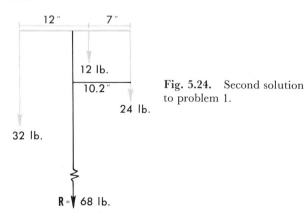

Fig. 5.24. Second solution to problem 1.

The following problem utilizes the principle of moments in determining the total exercise load on the quadriceps muscle in mechanical resistance exercise of the deLorme type.

3. Problem

Weights totaling 30 lb. are placed on the foot (Fig. 5.25). The leg and foot weigh 9 lb. The center of gravity of the leg and foot together lies 8 in. distal to the knee joint axis, and the exercise weights are 22 in. distal to the joint axis.

QUESTION.   Find the magnitude and action

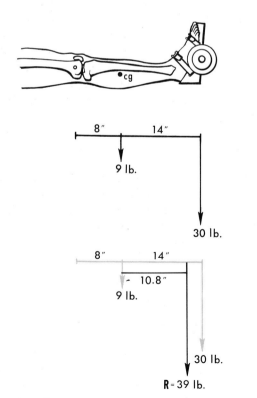

Fig. 5.25. Exercise load in problem 3; force diagram and solution.

line of the total load pulling downward against the knee extensor muscles.

SOLUTION.   Substituting in our formula, R = ΣF, we have

R = 30 + 9
= 39 lb. This force is acting downward.

Selecting the center of gravity of the leg and foot as moment center, we have

$$RX = 30 \times 14$$
$$39X = 420$$
$$X = \frac{420}{39}$$
$$= 10.8 \text{ in.}$$

Thus R lies 10.8 in. distal to the center of gravity of the leg and foot, and 18.8 in. distal to the knee axis. A useful term here is that the load moment acting to flex the knee is 733.2 inch-pounds (39 lb. × 18.8 in.). This means that the quadriceps muscle must produce a moment of more than 733.2 inch-pounds in order to extend the knee. Repeat this computation using the center of gravity of the weights as moment center.

4. Problem

In the examples so far all the forces have been acting on the same side of the moment center. Let us return to the first problem (on page 47) and take moments about the 12 lb. force. From our earlier computations we already know that R = 68 lb. and it is acting in a downward direction.

As before, we multiply the magnitude of each force by its distance from the selected moment center, keeping track of the direction of rotation about the point (Fig. 5.26). The rotations in the clockwise (CW) direction are added together (let us call them +); the counterclockwise (CCW) rotations are then subtracted from them. The result is the rotational effect of the entire system about the point selected. Here a positive answer indicates clockwise and a negative answer indicates a counterclockwise direction of rotation. According to the principle of moments, this result must be equal to the turning effect of the resultant about the same point.

$$RX = \Sigma M$$
$$68X = (24 \times 7) - (32 \times 12)$$
$$68X = 168 - 384 = -216$$
$$X = -3.2 \text{ in.}$$

Since the moment of the resultant is negative, we know that the turning effect is counterclockwise. We determine by inspection of the diagram that the resultant must lie 3.2 in. to the left of the moment center, or just where it has been all along. Here it causes rotation about the center in the same way as do the original forces. (Whether X lies to the right or to the left of the moment center must be determined by examination of the direction of rotation and is not obtained automatically through substitution in an equation.)

We see that the moment center could be selected anywhere along the object or even on a line projected out into space. The answer will be the same. This is the reason why many persons have pointed out the futility of trying to decide whether the axis should be considered at the ankle or at the metatarsophalangeal joints in analysis of tiptoe standing. It makes no difference in the analysis of forces. The moment center could just as well be located at the point of the tendo-Achilles insertion or somewhere outside the foot. (Fenn[5] has recently published an interesting discussion of this classic argument.)

5. Problem

Consider the forearm with the elbow flexed to a right angle. A 15 lb. weight is held in the hand, and the forearm and hand together weigh 3 lb. The biceps is contracting with a force of 70 lb. The position of these forces along the forearm is indicated in the diagram, in Figure 5.27.

QUESTION. Is the forearm flexing, extending, or remaining stationary?

SOLUTION. A line diagram will clarify the procedure. First, we may represent the known forces by vectors. Since the humerus touches the forearm it exerts force on it and must be represented by a vector. However, the effect of the humerus on the forearm is unknown; this vector will be labeled H and moments will be computed about this point. (Downward forces will be +).

$$R = \Sigma F$$
$$R = 3 + 15 - 70$$
$$R = -52 \text{ lb. (Upward, since the upward}$$
forces were made negative.)

In computing moments, clockwise moments will be positive, counterclockwise moments negative:

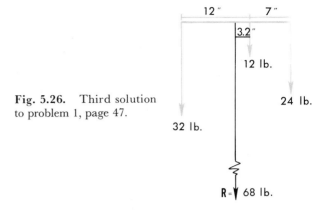

Fig. 5.26. Third solution to problem 1, page 47.

$$RX = (3 \times 6) + (15 \times 13) - (70 \times 2)$$
$$52X = 18 + 195 - 140$$
$$52X = 73 \text{ (Positive, therefore clockwise.)}$$
$$X = \frac{73}{52} = 1.4 \text{ in.}$$

Since R is directed upward, in order to make it tend to rotate clockwise about the moment center, the way the force system does, it must be placed 1.4 in. to the left of the joint center. The elbow is therefore being extended and we can assume that the biceps is contracting eccentrically (doing negative work) in lowering the 15 lb. weight in the hand.

Determination of the Center of Gravity. This problem of locating the action line of the resultant of a parallel force system is an important one. It is by means of this technique

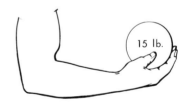

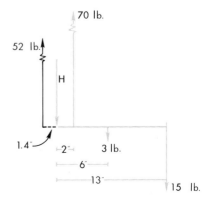

Fig. 5.27. Diagram of force system, problem 5.

that we locate the position of the center of gravity of a body. It was mentioned earlier (p. 12) that the center of gravity of an object is a point at the exact center of its mass. The force exerted by the object as a result of gravitational pull may be considered as a single force representing the sum of all the little individual weights within the object (Fig. 5.28). The magnitude of the single resultant force will equal the combined individual weights of the component units of the object. The action line of the resultant force will pass through a point about which all the moments of the individual weights on one side will be exactly equal to the combined individual moments on the other side of the point. Thus if the object is balanced on a knife edge or suspended at this point, it will remain level since the clockwise and counterclockwise moments on either side of the bearing point or fulcrum are equal. If an object is not symmetrical, the center of gravity or midpoint of its mass will be located toward the area of greater mass (or density) as in the baseball bat shown in Figure 5.29. This is because of the larger combined moments of the larger individual weights toward the heavier end of the object.

Suspending or balancing an object in one position locates the action line of the force of gravity with respect to that position. In order to find the exact position of the center of gravity along this line, it is necessary to rotate the object through an angle, preferably 90 degrees, and to suspend or balance it again in order to determine the action line of the resultant force in the new position. The intersection of this

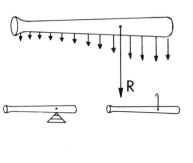
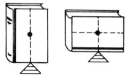

Fig. 5.29. Locating the single resultant force of gravitational pull on an asymmetrical object by balancing or suspending the object.

second action line of gravitational force with the original one gives us the location of the center of gravity of an object in which the forces are acting in a single plane (Fig. 5.29).

This same principle has been utilized in finding the center of gravity of the human body. As early as the 17th century Borelli,[6] an Italian mathematician, used this method. He first balanced a plank over a wedge (Fig. 5.30A). Borelli then placed the subject on the plank and adjusted the subject's position until he, too, was exactly balanced over the wedge. This indicated the height of the center of gravity of the subject between the soles of the feet and the crown of the head. The same principle can be used to determine the anteroposterior "balance" of the subject (in the sagittal plane) and the lateral distribution of weight on right and left foot (in the frontal plane) (Fig. 5.30B). The intersection of the three planes established by this technique gives us the exact center of gravity of the body. As was mentioned earlier, this point has been found to lie within the pelvis and is frequently described as being located just anterior to the second sacral vertebra.* A more practical means

* Early in the last century the Weber brothers[7] determined that the center of gravity lay 56.8 per cent of the distance from the soles of the feet to the top of the head. Other figures have been: 57.9 per cent (Harless[8]), 54.8 per cent (Braune and Fischer[9]) and 55 per cent of this distance (Hellebrandt and Franseen,[10] on women subjects). Many authors have stressed the variability of this figure according to the age, sex, and body build of the subject.

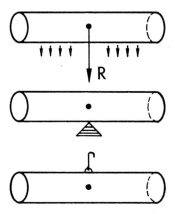

Fig. 5.28. Locating the single resultant force of gravitational pull on a symmetrical object by balancing or suspending the object.

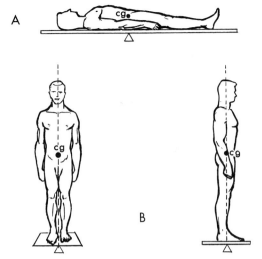

Fig. 5.30. A. Method used by Borelli to locate the
height of the center of gravity of the
body.
B. Same principle applied to locate the center of gravity with respect to the sagittal
and coronal planes.

than Borelli's for determining the body's center
of gravity, by the well-known board and scale
method, will be discussed under equilibrium
problems in the next section.

With a little practice it is not difficult to
visualize the center of gravity of objects, even
if we have no need to work out problems mathematically. Balancing a loaded tray with one
hand, for example, is a feat which requires that
the carrier size up the load properly. Counterforce can best be applied in lifting and carrying,
pushing and pulling, and the like when the
center of gravity of the object is taken into consideration. Disaster has resulted from errors in
judgment such as removing eggs from an egg
box from the wrong end first when the box is
balanced over the edge of a table; or taking
dishes off a partially-supported cafeteria tray in
the wrong order so that remaining items slide
about or completely disappear off the table.

The key to successful handling of patients
who need assistance in walking and moving
about is control and support at the pelvis, which
is the center of the body's mass. In helping a
patient to walk, the therapist may assist by
grasping the patient's belt or steadying the
pelvis (Fig. 2.17, p. 17).

A few problems are introduced now to help
us become better acquainted with resistance
offered by gravitational pull on the body seg-

ments in various positions. These will provide
further practice in locating the action line of the
resultant of a parallel force system. A careful
review of pages 129 to 137 in the appendix will
be helpful at this point before the remaining
problems in this section are undertaken. To
facilitate computations, a pattern for a manikin
has been supplied on page 134 for use with
standard ¼ inch graph paper. The dimensions
are based on Dempster's[11] measurements of air
force personnel, from which a drafting board
manikin was made for use in cockpit design. In
setting up a problem the student may position
the manikin on the graph paper and trace
around it. Consult page 15 for weight values,
and *indicate the vectors accurately* by drawing them
to scale with careful regard to all the characteristics of each force. A simple scale is suggested
on page 53 for use in problems involving body
weights. Average dimensions of the body and
location of centers of gravity are given on pages
134 to 137.

1. Problem

Patient A weighs 175 lb. The center of gravity
of his thigh lies 8.5 in. above the knee joint, and
that of the leg and foot 8 in. below it (Fig. 5.31).

QUESTION. Where does the center of gravity
of the entire lower limb lie in relation to the
knee joint?

SOLUTION. On the basis of Dempster's figures,
the thigh in this case weighs 17.0 lb. and the
combined leg and foot, 10.5 lb. Thus in our first
equation,

$$R = \Sigma F$$
$$R = 17.0 + 10.5$$
$$= 27.5 \text{ lb.}$$

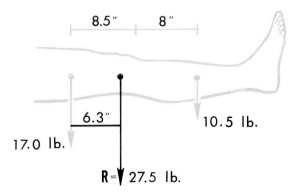

Fig. 5.31. Computation of single resultant force of the
lower limb and its position, problem 1.

Taking moments about the center of gravity of
the thigh,

$$RX = \Sigma M$$
$$27.5X = 10.5 \times 16.5 = 173.25$$
$$X = \frac{173.25}{27.5}$$
$$= 6.3 \text{ in.}$$

The center of gravity of the entire limb lies 6.3
in. distal to that of the thigh, or 2.2 in. proximal
to the knee joint in this case.

2. Problem

QUESTION.   Find the center of gravity of the
lower limb with the knee flexed to a right angle.
The person weighs 150 lb. Distances are given
in Figs. 5.32 and 5.33, and the thigh, leg and
foot weigh 14.5, 6.8, and 2.1 lb. respectively.

SOLUTION.   Here we will consider separately
the three component units—thigh, leg, and foot.
To find the center of gravity of a linked segment
which is flexed, it is necessary to determine the
resultant force with the object in two positions.
Beginning with the thigh horizontal,

$$R = \Sigma F$$
$$= 14.5 + 6.8 + 2.1$$
$$= 23.4 \text{ lb.}$$

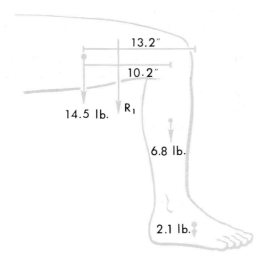

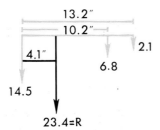

Fig. 5.32.   Center of gravity computation, problem 2.

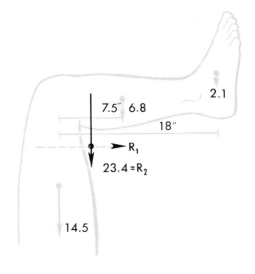

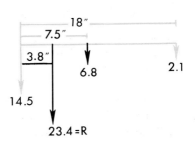

Fig. 5.33.   Second center of gravity computation with
part rotated 90 degrees; problem 2 continued.

and taking moments about the center of gravity
of the thigh, as a matter of convenience,

$$RX = (10.2 \times 6.8) + (2.1 \times 13.2)$$
$$23.4X = 69.4 + 27.7 = 97.1$$
$$X = \frac{97.1}{23.4}$$
$$X = 4.14 \text{ in.}$$

We must now find a second resultant in another
position in order to locate the precise center of
gravity point along the action line of the first
resultant. To do this we turn the object through
an arc of 90 degrees and repeat our procedure
(Fig. 5.33). The magnitude of the resultant has
already been found. Taking moments about the
thigh center,

$$RX = (6.8 \times 7.5) + (2.1 \times 18.0)$$
$$23.4X = 51.0 + 37.8 = 88.8$$
$$X = \frac{88.8}{23.4}$$
$$X = 3.8 \text{ in.}$$

Hence the center of gravity of the entire limb
when flexed in this position is 4.1 inches distal

to and 3.8 inches posterior to the center of gravity of the thigh. Let us call this point "c."

Notice that the point of application of the forces has no significance in taking moments since the moment arms to the action lines of all the forces lie along the same horizontal line.

Figure 5.34 shows that "c" lies just below a line drawn between the center of gravity points of the thigh and leg. If a combined center for the leg and foot had been used in these computations, "c" would lie on a line between these two initial points. This illustrates the observation made earlier that the center of gravity of a linked part which is flexed will lie between the two centers of the component parts, and slightly closer to the heavier part if they are unequal in mass.

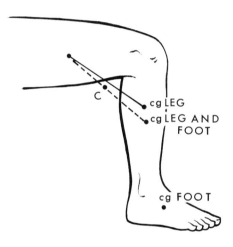

Fig. 5.34. Locating the single center of gravity of a flexed part (on a line between the respective centers of the component segments).

From the foregoing discussion, it may be seen that the center of gravity of the lower limb shifts backward as the knee is flexed and that of the upper limb shifts forward as the elbow is flexed. Since these limbs are suspended below the shoulder and hip axes like pendulums when the subject is upright, the lower limb will tend to move forward and the upper limb backward as the knee or elbow is flexed. In this way the center of mass remains directly below the supporting joint. If a load is carried in the hand, the arm moves still farther backward. These shifts in position lengthen important elbow and knee flexor muscles (biceps brachii, hamstrings) at their proximal ends so that they are better

able to exert tension and maintain the flexed position of the joint.

The solution of the preceding problem (No. 2) is diagramed in Figure 5.35 as it might be carried out with the manikin and graph paper. In the scale selected ¼ in. (one square) represents 1½ in. A method of tabulating data is suggested which will simplify the computations (Table 5.1); tabulation is useful whenever moments are found with the object in more than one position.

To simplify the procedure of finding a single center of gravity for linked segments, moments are taken about the center of one of the parts, in this case the thigh. This eliminates a moment value for this part since its moment arm is zero. Data may be tabulated conveniently as follows: each part is listed in column 1; its weight is entered in column 2; the distance from its center of gravity to the moment center (origin of the system) appears in column 3. (Here we have chosen the thigh center.) Moments of each force are found by multiplying the weight in column 2 by the distance to the origin in column 3. This moment value is entered in column 4. Totaling column 4 gives the total moment acting about the origin when the limb is in the position shown. Totaling column 2 gives the magnitude and direction of the resultant force. The distance to the action line of the resultant and therefore to the centroid is obtained by dividing the sum of the moments in column 4 by the resultant force magnitude in column 2. If we have been careful with the signs of the forces and moments, we can now locate the action line of the resultant, R_1.

In order to find the exact point of the center of gravity along the action line we must rotate the limb 90 degrees and repeat the process. We can extend the table to find the action line of the resultant, R_2, which lies at right angles to R_1. A fifth column shows the distances between the forces which are at right angles to the previous distances. Another moment column is obtained by multiplying these distances by the corresponding weights in column 2. Dividing the sum of the moments in column 6 by the total weight in column 2 again gives the position of the action line of the resultant force. The location of the center of gravity of the entire limb at the juncture of these two vectors is now completely defined.

Let us consider another position of the body and again find the center of gravity.

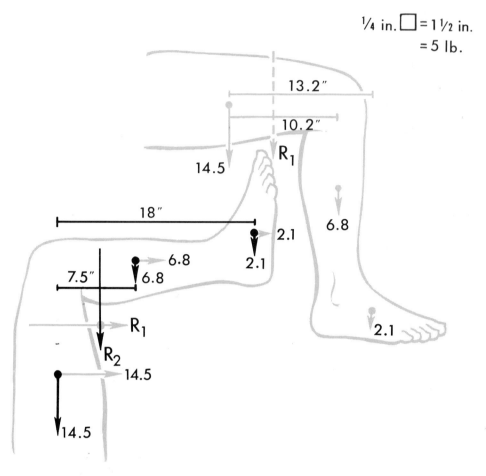

¼ in. ☐ = 1½ in.
= 5 lb.

Fig. 5.35. Locating the center of gravity of the lower limb flexed to 90 degrees.

Table 5.1. LOCATING THE CENTER OF GRAVITY OF A FLEXED LOWER LIMB

		R₁		R₂	
SEGMENT	WEIGHT (LB.)	DISTANCE (IN.)	MOMENT (IN.-LB.)	DISTANCE (IN.)	MOMENT (IN.-LB.)
Thigh	14.5	0	0	0	0
Leg	6.8	10.2	69.4	7.5	51.0
Foot	2.1	13.2	27.7	18.0	37.8
	23.4		97.1		88.8

$$R_1X = 97.1 \qquad R_2X = 88.8$$
$$23.4X = 97.1 \qquad 23.4X = 88.8$$
$$X = 4.1 \text{ in.} \qquad X = 3.8 \text{ in.}$$

3. Problem

Mr. X is seated with both arms flexed to 90 degrees (Fig. 5.36).

QUESTION. Find the center of gravity of the entire body when it is in this posture.

SOLUTION. Table 5.2 gives weights, distances, and tabulation of data in the solution of the problem. Our subject weighs 160 lb. Segment weights are shown in Figure 5.36. Since we

Table 5.2. LOCATING THE CENTER OF GRAVITY OF A SEATED SUBJECT

		R₁		R₂	
SEGMENT	WEIGHT (LB.)	DISTANCE (IN.)	MOMENT (IN.-LB.)	DISTANCE (IN.)	MOMENT (IN.-LB.)
Head and Trunk	98.4	0	0	0	0
Arm	8.6	6.7	57.6	−6.5	−55.9
Forearm	5.2	19.5	101.4	−8.0	−41.6
Hand	1.9	28.5	54.1	−9.0	−17.1
Lower Limb	45.9	13.0	596.7	+18.2	+835.4
	160.0		809.8		720.8

$$R_1X = 809.8 \qquad R_2X = 720.8$$
$$160X = 809.8 \qquad 160X = 720.8$$
$$X = 5.1 \text{ in.} \qquad X = 4.5 \text{ in.}$$

are dealing with two limbs, we have doubled the weights. Drawing the figure on ¼ in. graph paper will help to give us the necessary distances to solve the problem. In the previous problem we determined a single center of gravity point for the lower limb in flexion, so we can make use of this point now. Remaining centers are for the three upper limb segments, and the head and trunk.

The student should experiment for himself with center of gravity determinations of the body and its segments.

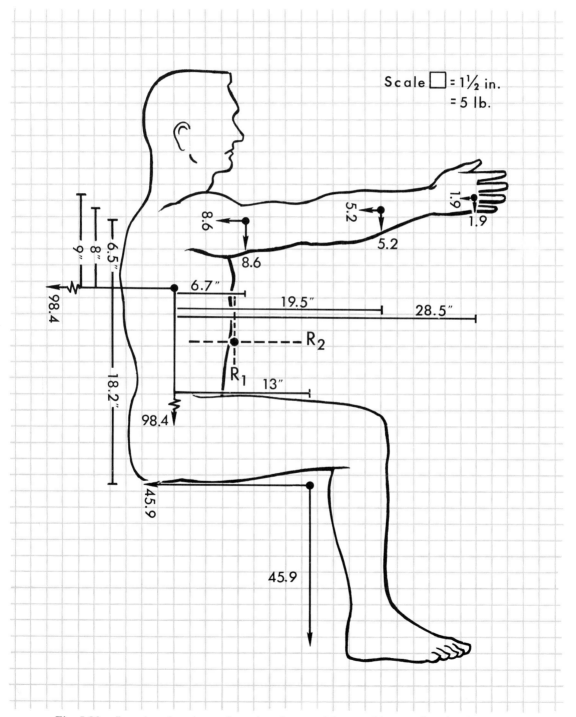

Fig. 5.36. Locating the center of gravity of a seated figure with arms flexed to horizontal.

You may wish to use measurements of weight and length made on yourself or another person as well as data given here. Begin to look for variations in body build among people and to make visual estimates of resistances of parts in terms of their weight and lever arms (gravitational moments, in other words). Notice differences in segmental proportions of children and adults, and estimate relative differences in gravitational moments corresponding to these variations in body size and shape.

In the following section, two methods will be suggested for checking experimentally on such estimates of body segment weights and on the theoretical computations done in this section.

Remember that in solving problems involving the body and its parts, moments can be computed about any arbitrarily selected point. The moment center selected will ordinarily depend on the nature of the problem. In finding the single center of gravity of the linked part in various positions, it is convenient to use the center of gravity of the heaviest component part as origin or moment center. This eliminates one large value from the computation. If pressure on a joint surface is being investigated, the point of application of force on the articular surface will probably best serve as origin of the system. Finally, if forces rotating a part are under investigation, such as muscle force, gravitational pull, or externally applied loads or manual forces, the axis of rotation of the part may be the most convenient moment center. In some cases the origin may be dictated by the forces which are known or unknown at the outset. Choice of the center will not alter the answer obtained in the solution of the problem.

Another possible form for a resultant of a parallel force system exists. It is called a couple. This will be discussed briefly at the end of this chapter.

Questions

1. Find the single resultant force for one upper limb in Figure 5.36. What *moment* must the shoulder flexor muscles exert to maintain this position of the limb?

2. Using the three component segments (arm, forearm, hand) find the center of gravity of the upper limb when it is in an extended position and when the elbow is flexed to various angles.

3. Repeat the preceding problem using different moment centers.

4. Repeat illustrative problem 3 with Mr. X's arms placed vertically above his trunk. Estimate first how you think the center of gravity will shift with this change in posture. Repeat your computations with the figure's knees extended.

5. Consider differences in your answers which might be expected with tall thin people and short fat people; with children.

6. Two common basic positions for therapeutic exercise are "hooklying," A, and supine lying, B (Fig. 5.37). Find the single resultant force equivalent to the three segments of the lower

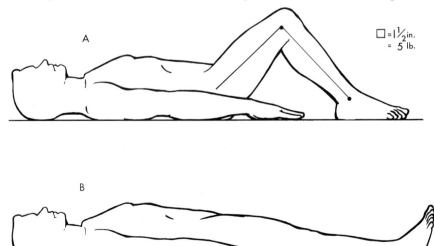

Fig. 5.37. Two starting positions for posture exercises.

limb in these two positions. Estimate the distances needed.

7. On the basis of your computations, which of the above positions might be more favorable as a starting position for "leg raising" exercises early in the recovery of a low-back patient? Why? (Compare the moment of gravitational pull on the limb in A and B.)

8. During leg raising, the abdominal muscles must stabilize the pelvis against anterior rotation caused by reverse action of the hip flexors (pulling on their origins). What moment must be exerted by the hip flexor muscles in order to lift:

    (a) one flexed lower limb
    (b) one extended limb
    (c) two flexed limbs
    (d) two extended limbs?

9. In figure A above, the knees are flexed to a right angle. What would be the moment of gravitational pull in leg raising exercises if the limbs were flexed to 110 degrees; to 65 degrees?

10. Which of the above positions would provide more stability for trunk flexion? Why?

11. Estimate the moment of gravitational pull opposing trunk flexion in the above figures (assume the moment center to be at the hip joints).

The Equilibrium Problem: Body Weight Determinations

The Equilibrium Problem. To make the resultant vanish for equilibrium in a parallel force system, the required equations are:

$$\Sigma F = 0$$
$$\Sigma M = 0$$

The sum of the forces and the sum of the moments about any point in the force system must equal zero. Since we now have two independent equations, we can solve for two unknown values.

Let us return to the problem of finding experimentally the location of the center of gravity of the body (Fig. 5.38). We obtain a board long enough for the individual to lie on, and place it on two "knife-edges" at either end. (These may be triangular blocks of wood or pieces of angle iron.) One end of the apparatus rests on a plat-

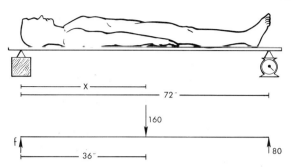

Fig. 5.38. Method of locating the body's center of gravity between the soles of the feet and crown of the head.

form scale and the other on a block. A zero reading on the scale can now be obtained which must be subtracted from subsequent readings to eliminate the effect of the weight of the board.

1. Problem

A man whose weight is 160 lb. lies on the board. We now have a parallel force system in equilibrium.

QUESTION. Find the action line of gravitational force pulling on the subject (in other words, his center of gravity with respect to this position).

SOLUTION. We have determined that the distance between the board supports is 72 in. For convenience we will compute moments around the support at "f." The scale reading is 80 lb. Applying the equations of equilibrium, we have

$$\Sigma M = 0 \text{ (CW moments positive)}$$
$$(160 \times X) - (72 \times 80) = 0$$
$$160X = 5760$$
$$X = 36 \text{ in.}$$

The action line of gravitational force lies 36 in. to the right of the moment center, "f." The position of this point as measured from the soles of the feet should be converted to a percentage of the total height of the individual for comparison with findings in the literature (see p. 50).

Although it may not particularly interest us in this case, we can easily find the reaction force under the board at "f." (The same method will be used later on to determine pressures in joints, a matter which does interest us.) Since $\Sigma F = 0$, and two of the three forces are known, we can solve for the third. If downward forces are $+$, then

$$160 - 80 - f = 0$$
$$f = -80 \text{ lb. (an upward force)}$$

If the subject now stands on the board facing the scale, the action line of the force of gravity in the sagittal plane can be determined in the same manner. Finally, he makes a 90 degree turn and faces forward, so that we may establish the action line in the frontal plane. The three planes established by this procedure intersect at the center of gravity of the body. The subject must be cautioned not to change his alignment in any of the three positions while measurements are being made, as this will shift the center of gravity.

The vertical projection of the center of gravity on the supporting surface can be determined by a simple experiment using the board and scale (Fig. 5.39). The subject, facing the scale, stands on a piece of paper and a tracing is made around his feet. The point at which the action line of gravitational force, acting at the body's center of gravity, falls in relation to the base is determined as before (from the body weight, the scale reading, and the distance between the knife edge supports). A line is drawn across the paper to indicate this position. The paper is then turned as the subject turns to face forward and the process is repeated. The intersection of the two lines indicates the point directly below the body's center of gravity. The first cross-line indicates body balance in the anteroposterior

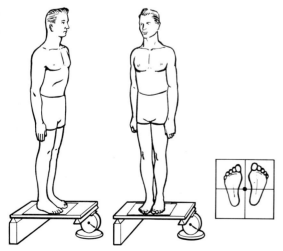

Fig. 5.39.   Locating the vertical projection of the gravity line in relation to the feet.

direction and the second, in the lateral direction. Hellebrandt[12] determined that this point commonly lay slightly forward and to the left of the center of the base of support (women subjects).

2. Problem

As another example of forces in equilibrium, suppose a patient is pushing his forearm downward against a sling to oppose a 20 lb. exercise weight (Fig. 5.40). The forearm is not moving and its weight is ignored.

QUESTION.   What is the isometric contraction force of the triceps and the compression force on the distal end of the humerus? (Distances are indicated in Figure 5.40.)

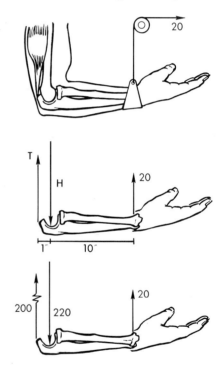

Fig. 5.40.   Diagram of forces, problem 2.

SOLUTION.   A free body diagram of the forearm helps in setting up the problem properly. The sling exerts an upward force of 20 lb. on the forearm. The direction and action line of the triceps muscle force is known but, since its magnitude is not, this will be labeled T. The vector H represents the humerus, pressing against the ulna.

Now, by applying to the figure the equations of equilibrium for a parallel force system, the magnitude of T and H can be found. Moments are taken around H:

$$\Sigma M = 0 \text{ (CW moments +)}$$
$$(1 \times T) - (10 \times 20) = 0$$
$$T = 200 \text{ lb.}$$

Next,
$$\Sigma F = 0 \text{ (Downward forces +)}$$
$$H - 200 - 20 = 0$$
$$H = 220 \text{ lb.}$$

This principle is used in so-called "objective" dynamometer testing of maximum voluntary isometric muscle contraction.[13] A sling or cuff is placed around the part with a line attached to a force-measuring device. The subject then pulls as hard as he can against this fixed resistance, and the meter reading is recorded. The product of the meter reading and the lever arm of the test force (distance from cuff to elbow axis) is the test *moment* applied to the forearm. This equals the *moment* of the muscle force. The meter reading is not a direct measure of the muscle force itself. This can be estimated, however, if one can estimate the lever arm of the muscle or muscles producing the force.

3. Problem

Mean isometric elbow flexion force of young adult men, with the elbow at a right angle, has been reported as 84 lb.[13] (Fig. 5.41). If the test strap at the wrist is placed 11 in. from the elbow axis and the action line of the principle flexor muscle is 2 in. from this axis, we can solve the following. (We are ignoring some of the flexor group and considering only the biceps brachii.)

QUESTION. What is the actual force of the flexor muscles?

SOLUTION. $\Sigma M = 0$. Computing moments

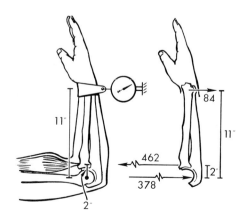

Fig. 5.41. Diagram of forces, problem 3.

about the elbow (CW moments +), $(84 \times 11) - (F \times 2) = 0$

$$924 = 2F$$
$$F = 462 \text{ lb.}$$

Thus when the elbow is at a right angle the principle elbow flexor must pull with a force of 462 lb. in order to produce a force of 84 lb. at the wrist. To find the forces on the humerus during the test:

$$\Sigma F = 0 \text{ (forces toward right +)}$$
$$84 - 462 + H = 0$$
$$H = 378 \text{ lb.}$$

It may be seen that this procedure, used in testing or exercise, subjects the articulating surfaces of the elbow joint to considerable compression force. When the relatively small area in contact is considered, the pressure per unit area appears enormous.

Nearly all muscles of the body do their work through bony lever systems. Hence the active tension they exert cannot be measured directly, but only by test forces applied to the levers they move. Since muscles attach close to joints, and resistances (gravitational pull or externally applied loads) are generally applied to a more distant point along the segment, muscles must act at a disadvantage as far as force requirement is concerned. The externally applied forces, on the other hand, usually enjoy a longer lever arm than do the controlling muscles. In their case a little force goes a long way. Let us see how this principle applies in a stretching exercise in the clinic.

4. Problem

A patient with a knee flexion contracture is sent to the physical therapist for stretching.

QUESTION. When a force of 15 lb. is applied at the ankle, what tension is placed on the hamstring muscles? Distances are given in Figure 5.42. The articular surface is considered to be the fulcrum.

SOLUTION. Taking moments about the knee joint.

$$\Sigma M = 0 \text{ (CW moments +)}$$
$$(18 \times 15) - (H \times 2) = 0$$
$$270 = 2H$$
$$H = 135 \text{ lb.}$$

Thus, with the knee at a right angle, the manual

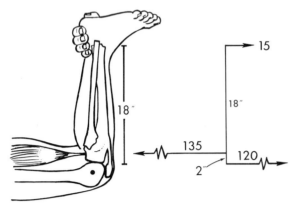

Fig. 5.42.   Diagram of forces, problem 4.

force applied is increased 9-fold on the tendons undergoing the stretch. A patient with a longer leg would experience even greater stretch force on the knee flexors. To determine the force in the knee joint structures at the fulcrum in this instance, we substitute in the formula,

$$\Sigma F = 0$$
$$15 - 135 + f = 0$$
$$f = 120 \text{ lb.}$$

Obviously, the physical therapist should apply manual force with great care. Often joint structures may require manual support during stretching procedures to make certain that the fulcrum is stabilized adequately. As mentioned earlier, the hand of the therapist may be placed close to the joint, decreasing the lever arm of the force and improving control of the motion (see p. 42).

Another example of the effectiveness of an externally applied force is the simple case of a weight held in the hand.

5. Problem

A man holds a 25 lb. weight in his hand. The forearm and hand weigh 4 lb. and the elbow is flexed to a right angle. Distances are given in Figure 5.43.

QUESTION.   Compute the necessary force required in the principal elbow flexors to support the load plus the weight of the forearm.

SOLUTION

$$\Sigma M = 0 \text{ (CW}$$
$$\text{moments } +)$$
$$(25 \times 14) + (4 \times 6) - (F \times 2) = 0$$
$$374 = 2F$$
$$F = 187 \text{ lb.}$$

The force on the elbow joint is given by

$$25 + 4 + H - 187 = 0$$
$$H = 158 \text{ lb.}$$

In this case, a force of more than seven times the load must be applied at the upper forearm to balance the weight in the hand. What would be the counterforce required of the elbow structures to support the weight if the forearm were hanging at the side? What type of force system would we be dealing with under these circumstances?

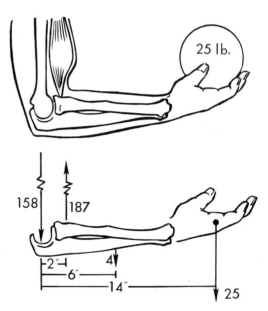

Fig. 5.43.   Diagram of forces, problem 5.

When manual pressure is applied to the end of a body segment as in stretching, manual muscle testing, or in the application of manual resistance during exercise, a small amount of external force is greatly magnified by the lever system. It has been pointed out that forces which "take hold of" the skeletal apparatus are usually enabled to act with much better leverage than the muscles which oppose them. Gravitational forces nearly always act with better mechanical advantage than do the anti-gravity muscles. However, this arrangement, while making large demands in force on the muscles, has an important advantage. It can be seen in Figure 5.44 that small excursions of the tendon or muscle cause wide arcs of movement of the distal end of the segment. The longer the segment the greater the excursion, and the faster the distal end of the segment reaches its goal. In

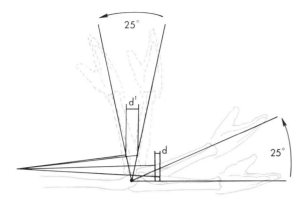

Fig. 5.44. Relation of lever length and angle of force application to speed and range of movement of a segment. The distance through which the muscle shortens during 25 degrees of movement of the forearm is greater near midrange than near extension.

other words, wide movements of the body can be made with speed, but at the expense of large muscle forces.

Notice also that the length of arc of movement of the segment is affected not only by the length of the part but by the angle of application of the controlling muscle force. A given unit of shortening (or lengthening) of the muscle produces the smallest arc of movement when the force is applied to the long axis of the part at nearly right angles. Or, conversely, when the segment travels through a total range of, let us say, 25 degrees (as in Fig. 5.44), less change in muscle length (d) takes place between 180 and 155 degrees in the total arc than between 100 and 75 degrees (d′). Stated in still another way, a given unit of muscle shortening causes the bone to move farther and faster when the angle of force application is small than when it approaches a right angle.

In previous sections we have dealt with theoretical weights of body parts. A simple way of checking these values is possible since "an object behaves as though its entire mass were acting at its center of gravity." We can now estimate quite accurately the location of center of gravity points in the segments of the limbs, and also centers of linked parts.

First Method of Weighing Body Parts. With the subject recumbent, place a sling around one limb at its center of gravity and suspend the sling from a scale (Fig. 5.45). If moments are taken about the proximal joint center in each case, the lever arm of the supporting force is equal to that of gravitational force.

Thus, the scale reading gives the weight of the part ($\Sigma M = 0$). (Some error probably results from the fact that the limb is attached to the body, but this error will be minimal if the subject is completely relaxed.)

Suppose the subject in Figure 5.45 is of average size and his upper limb weighs 8 lb. The center of gravity of the limb is 10 in. from the axis of rotation at the shoulder. Thus, gravity is exerting a clockwise moment of 10 × 8 = 80 in.-lb. about the shoulder. If we place the test sling at the center of gravity, the lever arm of the test force will also be 10 in. and the scale will read 8 lb. The counter-clockwise moment of the test force equals the clockwise moment of gravity about the shoulder, and if the lever arms of these opposing moments are kept the same (10 in.) the respective forces will also be the same (8 lb.).

Of course, in actual practice we do not know the weight of the limb at first. We apply the sling at the estimated center of gravity and the scale reading gives us the weight of the part. If we place the sling and scale at some other point along the part, we will expect a reading different from the true weight. If it is applied above the

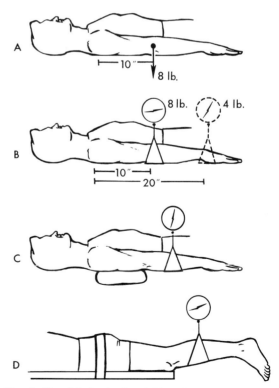

Fig. 5.45. Method of weighing body segments by sling suspension.

elbow where the lever arm is short, the scale reading will be higher; if the sling is applied to the forearm, the scale reading will be lower. At any point, the scale reading times the lever arm (distance to shoulder) will equal gravitational force times its lever arm. In the above example (Fig. 5.45B), if the sling is placed at the wrist 20 in. from the shoulder, we will obtain a scale reading much lower than the previous one; (20 in. $\times$ 4 lb. = 80 in.-lb.). In this case, to find the weight of the part from our scale reading, we will fill in the known terms in our formula, $\Sigma M = 0$. We have estimated the lever arm of gravitational pull on the limb to be 10 in. Then

$$(4 \times 20) - (G \times 10) = 0$$
$$80 - 10G = 0$$
$$G = 8 \text{ lb. (weight}$$
$$\text{of the limb)}$$

In problems of this sort, three values are known so we can solve for the fourth. We have the scale reading and can measure the distances from moment center to action line of the test force and to the center of gravity of the part; we can then solve for the part weight. In this weighing procedure the sling must support the full weight of the part. To obtain relaxation of the subject the segment proximal to the part involved must be completely supported (Fig. 5.45C). It is a good idea to stabilize the pelvis firmly before attempting to weigh the thigh or leg or entire lower limb (Fig. 5.45D).

Second Method of Weighing Body Parts. We return to the board and scale apparatus to compute partial body weights. (The platform scale must be sensitive and accurate.) The principle here is that as a segment shifts its position, the scale reading will change proportionately. For example, a 125 lb. subject lies supine on a board resting on knife edges which are 72 inches apart (Fig. 5.46).

Problem

QUESTION. Determine the weight of one lower limb.

SOLUTION. Find on a yardstick along the edge of the board a point in line with the estimated center of gravity of the limb. Have the subject flex the limb, find a second point in line with the new position of the center of gravity, and take the new scale reading. Then,

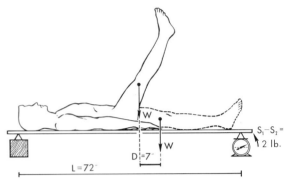

Fig. 5.46. Method of weighing body segments with board and scale.

$$W = \frac{L(S_1 - S_2)}{D}$$

in which
W = weight of the limb
L = length of board between the supports
S_1 = first scale reading
S_2 = scale reading with the part in the second position
D = horizontal distance through which the center of gravity traveled when the limb was moved.

(For further explanation of the formula see Appendix, p. 137).

In this instance the new scale reading was 56 lb. (a difference of 2 lb.), and the center of gravity shifted 7 in. Applying these values to the formula,

$$W = \frac{72(58 - 56)}{7}$$
$$W = 20.6 \text{ lb.}$$

Method two above may be checked against method one in finding experimentally the weights of the body segments. Finding the trunk weight is much easier by the second method. It is also of interest to weigh a part with the body in various positions, such as supine, sidelying, and prone, and to compare the values obtained. Values may be compared with the theoretical data of Dempster.

Examples from the Literature

A universally applied clinical example of the parallel force system is the so-called three-point pressure principle of brace design. The supporting forces of the brace are so arranged that two forces pressing against the trunk or limb are opposed by a third force which is located between the other two. Jordan[14] has explained this principle as follows:

"Three main forces . . . should be distributed over adequate surfaces or divided into a number of single units, the sum of which is equal in degree and direction to the desired or main force." The pressure per unit area is an important factor, as are the "give" or yield of the material in the brace parts, and the nature of the body tissues sustaining the pressure. Jordan emphasized that brace forces "must be active." In other words, the brace must fit well and do its job of immobilization or support of the body.

In a discussion of proper application of three-point pressure in bracing, Thomas[15] points out that the single opposing force is equal in magnitude to the two forces acting in the same direction. This is an important factor in skin pressure. Figure 5.47, redrawn from Jordan, illustrates the desirable three-point application of forces in spinal bracing: thrusts in the posterior direction against the pelvis and upper thorax are opposed by an anterior thrust against the spine. A poorly designed brace or cast will fail to provide the necessary forces at the proper levels. In B the brace is too low in front and the upper force is absent. In C the brace is too high in back.

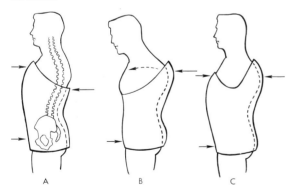

Fig. 5.47. A. Basic principle of 3-point pressure in bracing, applied to control of vertebral column alignment.
B. Stabilization inadequate because brace is too low in front, allowing upper trunk to move forward.
C. Stabilization inadequate because brace is too high in back, obtaining compression but not correction of alignment. (Redrawn from Jordan, Ref. 14, by permission of the pubisher.)

The same basic design is applied in leg bracing. In describing a leg brace for genu valgum Trosclair[16] states, "There are in use today various types of leg braces, but practically all types use the same basic three-point principle." These may have double or single uprights. In the brace shown in Figure 5.48, straps attach to the upright above and below the knee and buckle to the contoured medial knee cup. Pressure in this brace "is present at some of the most permissible places . . . at the thigh from below greater trochanter to just above the knee; at the lateral portion of calf (. . . not enough to place excessive pressure on the peroneal nerve); at the ankle (where some patients will require a pressure button); and last on the medial condyles of the knee where we do not have nerve or blood supply of superficial position."[16]

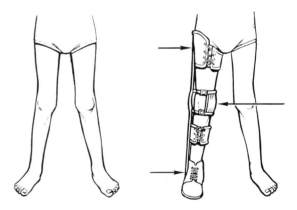

Fig. 5.48. Three-point pressure in bracing for genu valgum (knock knee) deformity.

Forces necessary for the correction of foot deformity are shown in Figure 5.49. The same principle of three-point pressure is utilized for this purpose. Plaster casts are applied for the correction of various types of club feet (Fig. 5.49A, B). T-straps on foot braces may be used to exert force in the control of foot or ankle alignment. Figure 5.49C shows a brace designed to correct foot pronation. In varus deformity of the foot the arrangement is reversed, with the upright inside and T-strap outside. "Twisters," sometimes used in cerebral palsy bracing to overcome internal rotation of the lower limb, are firmly anchored above and below the point at which pressure is exerted on the limb.

An interesting application of parallel forces is used by Arkin[17] in advancing the hypothesis

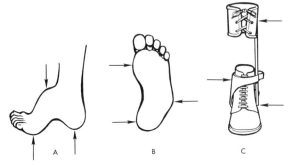

Fig. 5.49. Three-point pressure in correction of foot deformity.

    A. Sites of corrective forces in treatment of pes cavus.

    B. Forefoot adduction.

    C. Short leg brace with ankle T-strap to correct foot pronation on the left side. (Redrawn from Moore and from Phelps in Ref. 15, by permission of the publishers).

that deformity in idiopathic scoliosis is related to asymmetrical pressure on the vertebra, leading to arrest of epiphyseal growth. In the example cited, the vertebra at the apex of the curve is considered to be five vertebral diameters distant from the action of gravity (Fig. 5.50). The edge of the disk acts as a pivot point or fulcrum, a compression point. The distance from this point to the gravity line is X, and Y is the distance to the "ligament or supporting structure" on the convexity of the column, which is under tension. The seated figure represents the superincumbent weight, considered to be 50 lb. The ratio of distances involved is 5:1. Then,

$$\Sigma M = 0 \ (\text{CW forces} +)$$
$$(T \times 1) - (50 \times 5) = 0$$
$$T = 250 \text{ lb.}$$

and,

$$\Sigma F = 0$$
$$50 + 250 - f = 0$$
$$f = 300 \text{ lb.}$$

Both the superincumbent weight and the tension T developed in the ligamentous structures on the convexity of the curve exert a compression force on the edge of the vertebral body, which now becomes a fulcrum. This tremendous concentration of pressure, Arkin proposes, leads to arrest of vertebral epiphyseal growth and consequent wedging of the vertebral body.

Distribution of forces in cadaver feet was investigated by Manter,[18] who utilized a parallel force system in loading the specimens (Fig. 5.51). A metal bar was placed on the middle of

the upper surface of the talus. It was attached to the calcaneus posteriorly. The bar was positioned over the space between the second and third toes, forming a longitudinal "loading axis." A weight of 20 lb. was suspended on the bar "at a distance giving it a mechanical advantage of 3 at the point of contact with the talus." In other words, the weight was hung twice as far anterior to the talus as the distance from the talus to the calcaneus attachment posteriorly. The forces along the bar were then 20, 60, and 40 lb. respectively. Is there a parallel between this example and the static forces acting on the hip joint in the frontal plane (p. 44)? Might the direction of each vector as shown in Figure 5.51 be reversed? How would you "read" the figure in this case?

Many additional examples of parallel force systems can be found in the literature and in

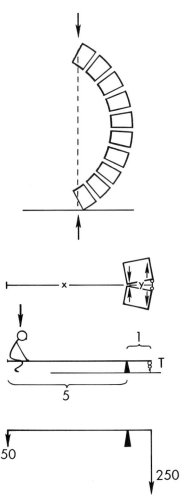

Fig. 5.50. Analysis of spinal deformity involving a parallel force system. (Redrawn from Arkin,[17] by permission.)

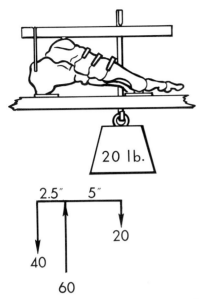

Fig. 5.51. Manter's method of loading cadaver feet for experimental determination of articular pressures. (Re-drawn, by permission.[18])

clinical situations. They are not difficult to analyze if the principle of moments is clearly understood.

Questions

1. Explain in your own words the principle of moments. Why is this so important in analysis of body movement?

2. How does the procedure of finding the resultant differ in the linear and in the parallel force systems?

3. What are the two requirements of equilibrium in a parallel force system? Explain them in your own words.

4. Give an example of decreasing or increasing an exercise load by changing the position of a body segment. Explain.

5. In a center of gravity experiment using the board and scale method, the gravity line of a 135 lb. subject bisects a 7 foot board.

(a) What is the scale reading?

(b) What would be the scale reading if the subject moved one foot closer to the scale?

(c) Would the scale reading increase or decrease if the subject faced the scale in this spot and flexed both arms to horizontal (toward the scale)?

6. Describe and explain two methods by which you might determine experimentally the weight of one of your lower limbs.

(a) What variation might be expected in a scale reading with the test sling at the knee and at the ankle? at the mid-thigh?

7. Explain why pressure against the joint surfaces is so great when relatively light loads are supported by the body parts.

(a) You now have sufficient information to solve the problem outlined on page 23. Try it.

Couples

Sometimes the simplest form to which a parallel force system can be reduced consists of two parallel forces equal in magnitude and opposite in direction but not in the same straight line. This type of resultant, which we have not encountered before, is called a *couple*. Since the two forces are applied in opposite directions some distance apart on the object, they combine to produce a turning effect when acting alone on the body. A couple is completely defined by its

magnitude—the product of one of the forces and the distance between them,

direction of rotation—clockwise or counterclockwise, and

aspect of the plane in which the couple acts.

Suppose nurses N and S in Figure 5.52 wish to turn a bed around. Each pushes with a force of 25 lb. at opposite ends of the bed in opposing directions. The forces are applied 5 feet apart, thus exerting a moment of 125 ft.-lb. in a counterclockwise direction. In this case the sum of the forces in the force system is zero; however, the sum of the moments is not zero but equal to the magnitude of the couple. The equations become

$$R = \Sigma F = 0$$

and

$$C = \Sigma M$$

1. Problem

Consider the parallel force system shown in Figure 5.53.

QUESTION. Find the resultant of the system.

SOLUTION. Let us make upward forces +;

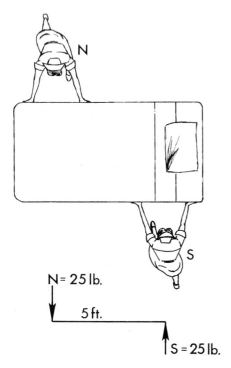

N = 25 lb.

5 ft.

S = 25 lb.

C = 5 ft. × 25 lb. = 125 ft. lb.

Fig. 5.52. Example of a couple, C, in which equal and opposite forces are applied to either end of a bed to turn it around. C = the product of one of the forces and the distance between them.

then,

$$R = \Sigma F = -10 - 20 + 25 + 5 = 0$$

Taking moments about point A, CCW moments +,

$$C = \Sigma M_A$$
$$= (5 \times 1) - (20 \times 3) + (25 \times 5) =$$
$$+70 \text{ ft.-lb.}$$

The resultant is a counterclockwise couple of 70 ft.-lb. If we select another center about which to take moments, for example, point B on the 25 lb. force, the answer will be the same:

$$C = (20 \times 2) - (5 \times 4) + (10 \times 5) =$$
$$+70 \text{ ft.-lb.}$$

The magnitude of the forces in the couple is unimportant so long as the product of one force and the intervening distance is 70 ft.-lb. Note that the forces in the couple must be directed to give counterclockwise rotation, since the answer is positive.

It is apparent that if all the forces in a force system are going in the same direction, the resultant cannot be a couple. Pure rotation can-

not take place unless there is a couple. If nurse N or nurse S in Figure 5.52 pushed alone, the bed would move sideways in addition to rotating about a central point.

Examples of arrangements of muscles that suggest the action of a couple include those bringing about axial rotation of segments, for example:

(1) Sternocleidomastoid and contralateral splenius capitis muscles act together to rotate the head about the axis between the first and second cervical vertebrae.

(2) External oblique and contralateral latissimus dorsi muscles rotate the thorax on the pelvis or vice versa. (The large central portion of the external oblique depends on the pull of the opposite internal oblique to accomplish axial rotation.)

(3) The horizontal component of the upper trapezius muscle pulls together with the serratus anterior (Fig. 6.28) to rotate the scapula upward in arm elevation and control its downward rotation. When the serratus anterior is paralyzed the arm cannot be lifted above shoulder level.

Another example is rotation of the pelvis in the sagittal plane around the frontal axis. Anterior tilting is accomplished by hip flexors and lumbar extensor muscles, and posterior tilting by anterior abdominal muscles and hip extensors.

When assisting a patient in walking, the physical therapist may apply manual guiding forces to rotate the thorax or pelvis in the manner of a couple, with one hand on each side of the part. Some manual stretches for scoliosis involve vigorous twisting forces applied to the trunk in opposite directions.

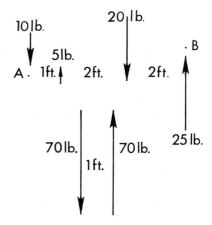

Fig. 5.53. Force system in which the resultant is a couple. C = 70 in.-lb.

Since the turning effect of a couple is measured by the product of one of the forces and the distance between them, a couple composed of small forces with a large distance between them is just as effective in producing turning as one in which the forces are large and the distance between them is small. For example, nurses N and S in Figure 5.52 would have to push twice as hard if they were only 2.5 ft. apart to produce the same effect on the bed. Turning forces applied to the large steering wheel of a bus or truck provide a greater moment for a given effort than would the same forces applied to the smaller wheel of an automobile. A large doorknob is easier to turn than a small bolt.

When the arm is rotated about its longitudinal axis, the total forces producing the rotation must constitute a couple; these forces must be acting at the glenohumeral joint since rotation takes place here. The forearm or thigh can also be rotated by muscle forces which produce a couple. The fact that muscle forces provide a couple to produce rotation can be demonstrated readily. Suppose the hand grasps a stick held at right angles to the forearm. If a single force is applied to one end of the stick, it will not prevent rotation of the forearm. Rotation can be prevented only if two forces of equal magnitude and opposite direction (a couple) are applied to the stick.

A couple acting on a body will always cause rotation of the body, or will tend to make the body rotate if the body is being held at rest by forces. The only method of maintaining equilibrium of an object on which a couple is acting is by means of another couple acting in the opposite direction and having the same magnitude. A couple cannot be held in equilibrium by means of a single force. The points of application of the forces that constitute a couple are immaterial in regard to the production of rotation. That is, the body will rotate regardless of where the couple is applied to it.

2. Problem

In Figure 3.6, p. 23, the distance between opposing forces P and F is 2 in. and the man weighs 160 lb.

QUESTION. If a total force of 40 lb. is applied to the pelvic belt through the lateral straps (20 lb. on each side), what is the magnitude of the

frictional force F and of the clockwise couple created by P and F? How is equilibrium maintained?

SOLUTION. $\Sigma F_x = 0$

$$P - F = 0$$
$$40 - F = 0$$
$$F = 40 \text{ lb.}$$

Next, we may take moments about either force (P or F) and get the following,

$$C = \Sigma M$$
$$C = 40 \times 2 = 80 \text{ in.-lb.}$$

A moment of 80 in.-lb. is tending to rotate the body clockwise. This requires that vertical forces W and N be slightly out of alignment to provide an equivalent counterclockwise moment on the body. From our equations we find that N must equal 160 lb. (since $\Sigma F_y = 0$) and the distance between W and N must be ½ in. (since the counterclockwise couple must equal 80 in.-lb. and each of the two forces is 160 lb.).

Example from the literature.   The free body diagram shown in Figure 5.54 is used by Radcliffe[19] to illustrate the force system acting at mid-stance when an amputee walks on a Canadian-type hip-disarticulation prosthesis. The forces acting on the amputee are exerted

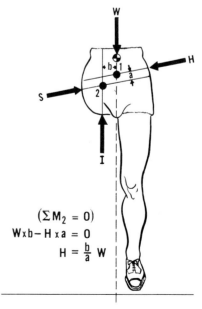

Fig. 5.54.   Force analysis of Canadian-type hip-disarticulation prosthesis. W (body weight) and I (prosthesis) acting at distance, b, are opposed by H and S (waist band tension and reaction of the opposite hip) acting at distance a.

by gravity and by the prosthesis at this point in the gait cycle, since the normal foot is off the ground. The four forces acting on the torso form two sets of force couples which act in opposite directions. The body weight W, acting through the center of gravity, and the upward supporting force I of the prosthesis form a clockwise couple. This would cause the pelvis to tilt downward on the side of the upraised normal foot if it were not opposed by a second couple acting in a counterclockwise direction. This is provided by tension in the waist band and by reaction against the normal hip. The four forces shown are of the same order of magnitude since the dimensions *a* and *b* are approximately equal.

Bibliography

1. Strait, L. A., Inman, V. T., Ralston, H. J.: Sample illustrations of physical principles selected from physiology and medicine. *Amer. J. Physics, 15*:375–382, 1947.
2. Storms, H. D.: Industrial rehabilitation. *Phys. Ther. Rev., 31*:355–6, 1951.
3. Inman, V. T.: Functional aspects of the abductor muscles of the hip. *J. Bone Joint Surg. (Amer.), 29*:607–619, 1947.
4. Blount, W.: Don't throw away the cane. *J. Bone Joint Surg. (Amer.), 38*:695–708, 1956.
5. Fenn, W. O.: Mechanics of standing on the toes. *Amer. J. Phys. Med., 36*:153–156, 1956.
6. Borelli, G. A.: De Motu Animalium. Lugduni Batavorum, 1679.
7. Weber, W., and Weber, E.: Machanik der menschlichen Gehwerkzeuge. Göttingen, Dieterich, 1836.
8. Harless, E.: Die statischen Momente der menschlichen Gliedmassen. Akad. d. Wissensch. zu München, Abhandl. d. mathem.-physik. Klasse d. Kgl. Bayer, 8, 1857.
9. Braune, W. and Fischer, O.: Über die Lage des Schwerpunktes des menschlichen Körpers. vol. XV: Abh. Math. Phys. Klasse d. Kgl. Sachsen, Ges. d. Wiss. Leipzig, S. Hirzel, 1889.
10. Hellebrandt, F. A., and Franseen, E. B.: Physiological study of vertical stance of man. *Physiol. Rev., 23*:220–225, 1943.
11. Dempster, W. T.: Space requirements of the seated operator. *WADC Technical Report, 55*:159, 1955.
12. Hellebrandt, F. A., and Fries, E. C.: The constancy of oscillograph stance patterns. *Physiol. Rev., 22*:17–22, 1942.
13. Williams, M., and Stutzman, L.: Strength variation through the range of joint motion. *Phys. Ther. Rev., 39*:145–152.
14. Jordan, H. H.: Orthopedic Appliances. New York, Oxford Univ. Press, 1939.
15. *Orthopedic Appliances Atlas.* Vol. I, Part 3, Appliances. Ann Arbor, J. W. Edwards, 1952.
16. Trosclair, M. J.: Corrective braces in knee curvatures. *Braces Today,* Dec. 1959, Newsletter of the Pope Foundation, Inc. (reprinted from the *Orthopaedic and Prosthetic Appliance Journal,* June 1959).
17. Arkin, A. M.: The mechanism of the structural changes in scoliosis, *J. Bone Joint Surg. (Amer.), 31*:519–528, 1949.
18. Manter, J. R.: Distribution of compression forces in the joints of the human foot. *Anat. Rec., 96*:313–321, 1946.
19. Radcliffe, C. W.: The biomechanics of the Canadian-type hip-disarticulation prosthesis. *Artificial Limbs, 4*:29–32, No. 2. Published by the Prosthetics Research Board, National Research Council, Washington, D. C. Autumn, 1957.

CHAPTER SIX

Composition and Resolution of Forces

In the preceding chapters we have considered force systems in which all the forces are parallel or in a line with one another. Obviously, in many situations this is not the case. For example, in the body, muscles are arranged so that their action lines are applied at many different angles to the bones. Furthermore, as a segment moves through its range of motion, the action line of a given muscle attaching to the part constantly changes. External forces are applied from many directions. Therefore we must have methods for dealing with forces which are not arranged in linear or parallel fashion.

In solving problems in biomechanics, the primary task is to recognize the factors involved and to properly set up the problem for solution. The setup of the problem as a free body diagram is then converted to mathematical expressions which can be solved. In setting up problems involving concurrent and general co-planar force systems, one or both of two basic procedures may be necessary, namely:

(1) Adding two or more vectors together so that their combined effect is shown by a single vector. This is known as *composition of forces.*

(2) Replacing a single vector by two or more equivalent vectors, whose combined effect is equal to that of the original force; this is termed *resolution of a force.*

In this chapter we will discuss these basic procedures preparatory to analyzing the force systems to which they apply.

Composition of Forces

We have already been introduced to composition of forces in finding the resultant in the linear force system. In that situation the forces on the object acted along the same line. If they had the same direction they were added together to give us the resultant. If they acted in opposite directions, they were given + and − signs and added algebraically. In the graphic solution, vectors in one direction were subtracted from vectors in the opposite direction and the resultant vector was obtained by drawing a line from the beginning of the first vector to the end of the last one (Fig. 6.1).

Now we must add vectors which are not parallel. To find the resultant here we can make use of the Parallelogram Law, which permits a graphic solution, or its corollary, the Triangle Law, which permits both graphic and algebraic solutions.

Suppose we wish to find the resultant of two forces whose action lines intersect at an angle theta (θ). The magnitudes of the forces are P and Q. Composition (or addition) of the two forces can be accomplished by constructing a parallelogram with the forces as its sides (Fig. 6.2). From any arbitrarily selected point, we draw vectors representing each of the two forces. The vectors must be drawn in such a fashion that both arrows are directed away from the selected point. The length and direction of the vectors must accurately represent the original forces. Now the other two sides of the parallelogram can be constructed. A line drawn from the initially selected point to the opposite corner of the parallelogram gives the magnitude and direction of the resultant force, R, which will have exactly the same effect on the object as the two original forces combined, if R is transposed to pass through the point where the action lines of the original forces intersect.

A graphic illustration of this principle has been suggested in which nurse N pushes due north on a child's crib while nurse E is pushing it east with slightly more force[1] (Fig. 6.3). They will together move the crib in the same direction as nurse F alone who pushes in a northeasterly direction. The parallelogram in Figure 6.3 demonstrates that in moving the crib a given distance, the combined magnitudes of the forces of the nurses pushing north and east are greater

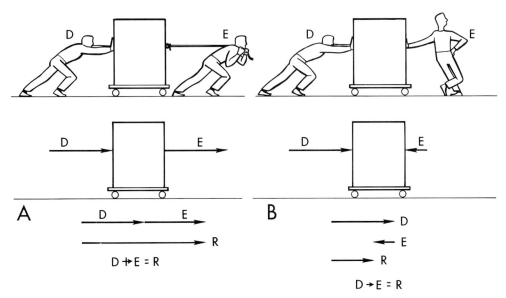

Fig. 6.1. Addition of vectors to find the total effect of two linear forces. In A, forces D and E are added to find the resultant, R. In the second figure, E must be subtracted from D since the forces are opposed. (⇴ indicates addition of vectors; → represents vector subtraction).

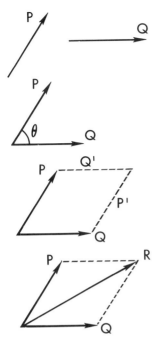

Fig. 6.2. Construction of a parallelogram to determine resultant vector, R, of two forces, P and Q, whose action lines form angle theta (θ).

than the single equivalent northeasterly force, F. In other words, part of a force is "wasted" when its action line is not in the direction of movement of the object.

Obviously when the action line of the force can be controlled, effort need not be exerted inefficiently. When one pulls or pushes an object, the force can be applied in the desired direction

of movement. This is usually true in the case of externally applied manual forces. However, the action line of muscles acting internally on the bony segments is fixed by their anatomical attachments. Thus, they must often pull in a line other than in the direction of movement, and some of their effect is "wasted." The same is true of gravitational force, whose action line and direction can never be changed from vertical and downward. As a body segment moves through space, the action line of gravity constantly changes with respect to the long axis of the moving segment. When the part is horizontal, gravity pulls at a right angle; in other positions the angle is less than 90 degrees.

To illustrate, in Figure 6.4*A* gravitational and muscle forces are maximally effective since they are pulling in the direction of motion, at right angles to the long axis of the part. In *B*, part of the force is "wasted," or not effective for rotating the part. Since the body parts are constantly moving in space, the forces controlling their motion are usually *not* acting in the direction of the motion. Two or more forces must therefore combine their actions to effect the desired movements. This involves composition of forces, usually combinations of gravity, joint, and muscle forces.

Some examples of composition of forces in the action of muscles are the following:

(1) The anterior and posterior parts of the deltoid muscle acting alone will flex and extend the arm in the sagittal plane (Fig. 6.5). By their

Fig. 6.3. A force is most effective when applied in the desired direction of motion, as in the case of F shown here. Two or more forces can be combined to obtain the desired direction, but with some waste of effort: N ⊹ E = R. Dotted arrow indicates direction of motion of the object. (Adapted from Flitter.[1])

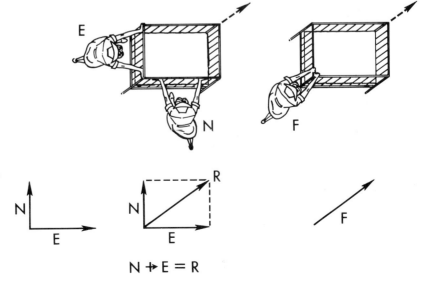

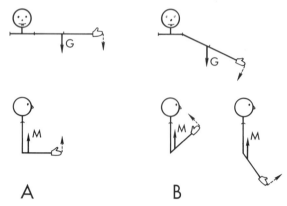

Fig. 6.4. Efficient and "wasteful" application of gravitational, G, and muscle, M, forces. Dotted arrow indicates direction of motion of the segment. In A, the forces applied are fully effective for rotating the segment, while in B a portion is lost.

combined action, pulling on the deltoid tubercle of the humerus, the two portions of the muscle can abduct the arm in the frontal plane.

(2) The clavicular and sternal portions of the pectoralis major muscle, acting together, can draw the arm across the trunk in horizontal adduction (Fig. 6.6). Notice the similarity to the structure and action of the trapezius muscle on the posterior chest wall.

(3) The two heads of the gastrocnemius muscle, pulling in lateral and medial directions, together exert an upward force on the Achilles tendon (Fig. 6.7). Compare this with a dorsal interosseus muscle (Fig. 6.29).

Many additional examples of muscle pairs or separate divisions of the more extensive muscles could be cited here. Muscles that act together to create a resultant force in the manner described

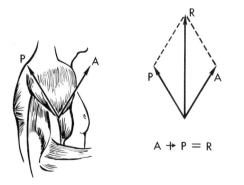

Fig. 6.5. Example of composition of muscle forces to produce a single resultant force. P and A represent the pull of the posterior and anterior deltoid muscle fibers to produce arm elevation. (⇸ signifies vector addition.)

have been termed "helping synergists" in the field of kinesiology (*syn*, with; *ergon*, work—to work with). Synergistic action is characteristic of fan-shaped muscles and certain opposing groups, such as:

(1) Anterior and posterior parts of the gluteus medius in hip abduction.

(2) Evertors and invertors of the foot in dorsiflexion or plantar flexion.

(3) Abductors and adductors of the wrist acting in wrist flexion or extension.

(4) Upper and lower trapezius in scapular adduction.

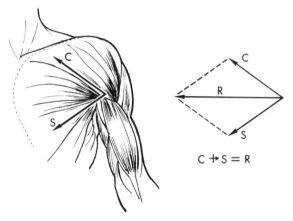

Fig. 6.6. Clavicular and sternal portions of pectoralis major together produce a single force acting horizontally across the chest (C ⇸ S = R).

Braus[2] presents a diagram of the direction of force exerted by individual muscles passing over the wrist joint (Fig. 6.8). The figure shows that many combinations of forces can be applied to move the hand. The directions of motion possible are limited only by the joint structures.

In the foregoing examples of combined muscle forces, the magnitudes of the force values have to be estimated as there is no practical way of measuring them directly.*

When vectors are shown in their actual position, as in a free body diagram, they are called *localized vectors*. When they are drawn parallel to their actual positions, as in the construction of the parallelogram, they are called *free vectors*.

* Forces have been measured directly on amputees who have muscle tunnels in such muscles as the pectoralis major, biceps brachii and triceps. However, this is a very unusual circumstance and it is likely that these values are not equivalent to maximum contraction forces of normal muscles.

Figures made of free vectors are called *vector diagrams*. Free vectors show all the characteristics of the forces except the correct position of the action line. To place it in its correct position, the resultant determined by the parallelogram must be drawn through the point of intersection of the two localized force vectors on the line diagram. The action lines of these forces may have to be extended to determine the point of intersection.

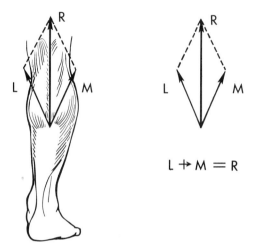

Fig. 6.7. Medial, M, and lateral, L, heads of gastrocnemius together pull upward on the tendon of Achilles.

Suppose we wish to find the equivalent single pull on the patella equal to the force of the distal vastus lateralis and medialis muscles. We draw a diagram of the patella and add the estimated muscle forces as localized vectors (Fig. 6.9*A*). Constructing a parallelogram of forces (vector diagram) enables us to determine the magnitude and direction of R (Fig. 6.9*B*). The action line of R is then located on the patella by extending the action lines of the localized vectors L and M until they intersect. It is obvious that composition of parallel forces would not be possible by this means.

Another approach to composition of forces is by means of the Triangle Law. This simply makes use of one-half of the parallelogram to determine the resultant R, and it will give us precisely the same characteristics of R (Fig. 6.10). Vectors representing the two forces are drawn with the beginning of one vector attached to the end of the preceding one. Then the line from the beginning of the first to the end of the second represents the resultant in magnitude

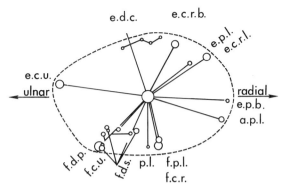

Fig. 6.8. Location of muscle forces at the wrist: *e.d.c.*, extensor digitorum communis; *e.c.r.l.* and *e.c.r.b.*, extensor carpi radialis longus and brevis; *e.p.l.* and *e.p.b.*, extensor pollicis longus and brevis; *a.p.l.*, abductor pollicis longus; *f.p.l.*, flexor pollicis longus; *f.c.r.* and *f.c.u.*, flexor carpi radialis and ulnaris; *f.d.p.* and *f.d.s.*, flexor digitorum profundus and superficialis; *p.l.*, palmaris longus; *e.c.u.*, extensor carpi ulnaris. (Adapted from Braus.[2])

and direction. It must, however, be moved parallel to itself to pass through the point of intersection of the action lines of the original forces acting on the line diagram, as in the case of the parallelogram solution.

In this approach, we can find an algebraic solution as well as a graphic one, since two sides of the triangle, the force magnitudes, and the angle included between them are known.*

We may use the Triangle Law to find the resultant pull of two parts of a muscle or of two synergistic muscles. For example, consider again the pectoralis major muscle (Fig. 6.6). Vector S in Figure 6.11, representing the sternal portion of the muscle, is placed at the tip of vector C, which represents the clavicular part. The resultant of both forces is then a vector from the beginning of C to the tip of S. Adding three or more forces involves merely an extension of the Triangle Law.

Examples from the literature. Two illustrations of composition of vectors will be given here. Many more examples can be found without difficulty.

* Making use of the cosine law of trigonometry we obtain $R = \sqrt{P^2 + Q^2 - 2 PQ \cos \theta}$ where P and Q are the original force magnitudes and θ is the angle between them. The angle ϕ between the resultant and the force, Q, is obtained from the sine law: $\sin \phi = (P/R) \sin \theta$. While the Parallelogram and Triangle Laws are basic to the subject of mechanics, we will generally not apply them directly in the form shown.

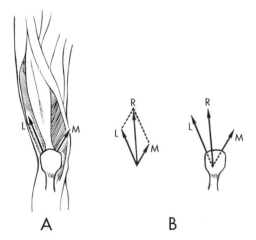

Fig. 6.9.   In locating the single resultant vector, R, of the combined vastus lateralis, L, and medialis, M, muscle forces on the patella, their action lines are extended to the point of intersection.

When Russell traction is used to immobilize a fractured femur,[3] the patient's limb is suspended as shown in Figure 6.12. The thigh is maintained at an angle of 20 degrees with the horizontal plane, or with the bed, so that the relation of the pulley ropes to the alignment of the limb remains constant. In the case of an adult patient a load of 8 to 10 pounds is applied to the pulley system. The force distal to the foot is nearly doubled by the arrangement of the ropes (Q, S). This force reaches the femur through the leg, while an upward force, P, is applied directly to the knee by means of a sling.

The vector diagram shows that the resultant force is in line with the femur. The counterforce balancing the pulley rope is provided by the patient's weight and the pull of the thigh and leg muscles. How would the resultant force on the femur be affected if the patient were allowed to slide down toward the foot of the bed? Why would it be dangerous to allow this to happen?

In the study of hip abduction muscle force, which was mentioned earlier (p. 45), Inman[4] and co-workers determined the action lines of the gluteus minimus, gluteus medius, and tensor

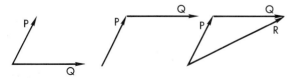

Fig. 6.10.   Use of the Triangle Law in composition of vectors: P → Q = R.

fasciae latae by inserting wires in cadaver muscles and making roentgenograms. (The problem involved only forces in the frontal plane.) Magnitudes of force were then determined by weighing the muscles and computing their average ratios of mass. That is, the mass of each was compared with the total muscle mass of the group. These ratios were found to be:

tensor fasciae latae	1 : 7
gluteus medius	4 : 7
gluteus minimus	2 : 7

The action line and magnitude of the resultant force were then used to compute the torque applied by the hip abductor musculature and iliotibial band in stabilizing the pelvis in the frontal plane. Figure 6.13 shows the pelvis tilted upward 15 degrees. In this position the moment of gravity is said to be resisted by the muscles alone with no assistance from the iliotibial band.[4] The figure shows the magnitude and direction of the resultant force being applied to the pelvis by the three muscles.

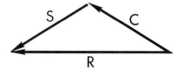

Fig. 6.11.   Use of the Triangle Law to find a resultant: C → S = R. The diagram is based on Figure 6.6.

Resolution of a Force

The process of resolving a force into two or more components is just the reverse of composition. Here we replace the original force by two or more equivalent forces. We have seen in the previous section that any pair of concurrent forces has a resultant. Conversely, any single force can be considered to be the resultant of a pair of concurrent forces, but in this case there is endless variety. That is, parallelograms can be constructed about the original force in many ways so that infinite pairs of components are possible. Each component may in turn be resolved into two or more components, so that three or more forces may be the equivalent of the original force (Fig. 6.14). The only rule is that components, when added in a vector diagram, must begin where the original force begins, and end where it ends. The forces from the

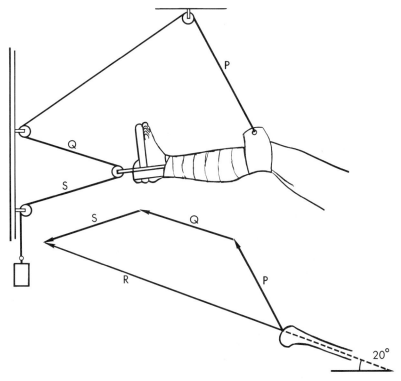

Fig. 6.12. Russell traction for immobilizing femoral fractures. The resultant traction force applied to the femur is determined by the ropes P, Q, and S. Force R, acting on the limb, is obtained graphically by a vector diagram. (Redrawn from Flitter.[1])

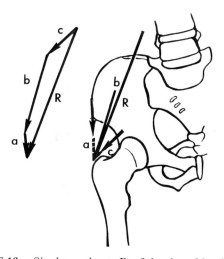

Fig. 6.13. Single resultant, R, of the three hip abductor muscles stabilizing the pelvis in the frontal plane; vectors a, b, c represent force of tensor fasciae latae, gluteus medius and gluteus minimus respectively. Here the pelvis is tilted upward 15 degrees, a position in which the moment of gravity on the pelvis in unilateral weight-bearing is said to be resisted by muscles alone without help from the iliotibial tract. (Inman et al.[4])

vector diagram will have to be moved to a parallel position, intersecting at a common point on the action line of the original force in the space diagram.

There is absolutely no limitation to the magnitude or direction of the components. One or more may be greater than the original force. The selection and arrangement of components of a force is determined by the problem to be solved.

In our work the most useful resolution of forces into components involves *determination of rectangular components*. Rectangular components lie at right angles to each other. When two lines are drawn forming a right angle with each other on the original force, the original force becomes the hypotenuse of a right triangle (Fig. 6.15C, D). Rectangular components must always be smaller in magnitude than the original force. Since we are always dealing here with a right triangle, we may use certain laws of trigonometry in arriving at algebraic solutions to problems. But first, consider some graphic illustrations in biomechanics.

76 BIOMECHANICS OF HUMAN MOTION

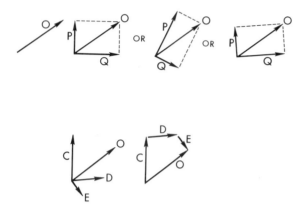

Fig. 6.14. Resolution of forces: Construction of equivalent vector pairs or polygon figures of three or more vectors equivalent to the original force, O. In the lower figure, to determine whether forces C → D → E = O (the original force), some of the vectors must be moved and placed parallel to themselves in the vector diagram.

(1) When the biceps brachii tendon is applied at right angles to the forearm, the entire force tends to rotate the part about the elbow (Fig. 6.15A). However, when the tendon is applied at an angle of 45 degrees to the long axis of the part (Fig. 6.15B), some of the force is acting in the direction of rotation of the segment and some is pulling the forearm upward toward the elbow joint. In kinesiology, the component which tends to rotate the part is called the "rotational" or rotatory component; the other is the "stabilizing" component, which compresses the joint sur-

faces or, in some cases, pulls them apart. We will label these components of the original force T and S respectively.

When the angle of application of the force is 30 degrees, a still smaller proportion of the force is available for rotation and more is "wasted" in compression of the joint. In Figure 6.15C, in which the angle of force application is 45 degrees, component vectors T and S are equal in magnitude. When the angle of force application is 30 degrees (Fig. 6.15D), vector S is larger than T. If the angle were more than 45 degrees, T would be larger than S.

In constructing the parallelogram, the original force is shown as a localized vector drawn to scale on a line diagram, as in Figure 6.15. Rectangular components are then drawn to determine the proportion of the force acting in the direction of movement of the part, and the force in line with the segment. Component T is drawn at a right angle to the long axis of the part and thus forms one side of a right triangle. Component S lies along the segment and shows us the compression force in the joint. The scale values of T and S will correspond to that of the original force in the graphic solution to problems. (Can you see that T is equivalent to the "side opposite" the angle we are dealing with in the right triangle formed, and that S is the "side adjacent"?)

(2) Suppose we wish to find the rotational and compressional forces resulting from the

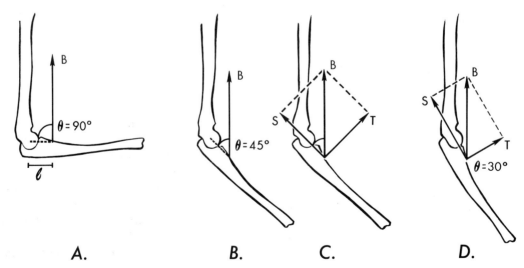

Fig. 6.15. In A, where θ = 90 degrees, all the force of B is rotatory. In C and D, rectangular components of the biceps pulling at angles of 45 and 30 degrees to the long axis of the forearm are shown. T and S are rotating and stabilizing components respectively. In C, T and S are equal, while in D, S becomes larger than T.

hamstrings acting at an angle of 45 degrees with the long axis of the leg. Rectangular components for the hamstrings are constructed in Figure 6.16 to show the characteristics of the two components of H. In this case they are equal in magnitude.

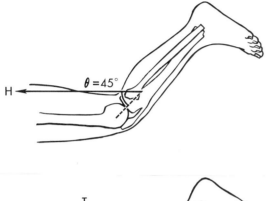

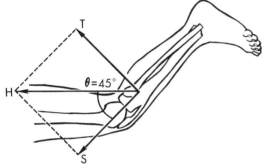

Fig. 6.16. Rectangular components of the hamstring muscle group, which is pulling on the leg at an angle of 45 degrees. T = rotating and S = stabilizing components of H.

(3) As a further example, the thrust of the heel against the ground at the beginning of the stance phase in walking can be resolved into rectangular components (Fig. 6.17). The horizontal force, X, must be opposed by frictional ground force, and the vertical component, Y, must be opposed by an adequate upward force of the ground or floor. Note in the second figure the effect of a longer step. There is no change in the magnitude of the component vector Y, as shown in the diagram, since this force is determined by body weight. However, the direction and magnitude of O and X are affected by step length.

In the algebraic solution of problems involving rectangular components, we use the trigonometric functions called sines and cosines (abbreviated sin and cos). These are based on the constant relationship of the two sides of a

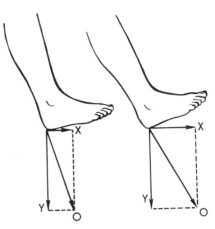

Fig. 6.17. Vertical, Y, and horizontal, X, components of force O acting against the ground at heel strike in walking. Relative magnitudes of the components depend on the angle of force application, which is related to step length. The angle made by O and Y is θ (see text p. 79.)

right triangle to the hypotenuse when one angle is specified.

A series of triangles will illustrate these relationships and how they vary with a change in the angle concerned (Fig. 6.18). If this principle is clear so that the sine and cosine values can be

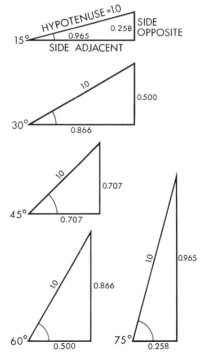

Fig. 6.18. Ratio of sides of a right triangle corresponding to given angles. The value of the hypotenuse is 1.0.

used with understanding, the student will be less likely to make mistakes than if he merely copies the values from a table without visualizing these relationships. The sine of the angle specified is the ratio of length of the "side opposite" the angle to the hypotenuse. In the figure shown,

$$\text{sine } 15° = \frac{\text{side opposite}}{\text{hypotenuse}} = 0.258$$

In other words, the side opposite the angle is 0.258 times the length of the hypotenuse when the given angle is 15 degrees. When the specified angle is 30 degrees, the "side opposite" is 0.500 times the hypotenuse.

In these examples the "side adjacent" to the angle specified also bears a relationship to the hypotenuse which is expressed as the cosine of the angle:

$$\cos 15° = \frac{\text{side adjacent}}{\text{hypotenuse}} = 0.965$$

When the angle is 30 degrees the cosine becomes 0.866.

Although we will not ordinarily have occasion to use it, the third relationship is the ratio of

$$\frac{\text{side opposite}}{\text{side adjacent}} = \frac{\sin}{\cos}$$

This is known as the tangent of the angle (abbreviated tan).

No matter what scale is used to represent values of length or force, the *ratio* of the respective sides of the right triangle remains the same for any specified angle (Fig. 6.19). This relationship is what interests us in dealing with rectangular components of a force.

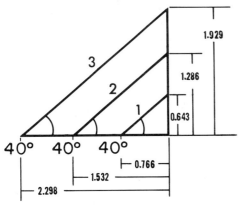

Fig. 6.19. Ratios of sides are constant for a given angle in right triangles of any size.

It will be useful to learn the following sines and cosines of angles. A complete table is given in the Appendix on page 139.

ANGLE	SINE	COSINE
0°	0	1.000
15°	0.258	0.965
30°	0.500	0.866
45°	0.707	0.707
60°	0.866	0.500
75°	0.965	0.258
90°	1.000	0

If values of one angle and one side or the hypotenuse of a right triangle are known, the rest of the triangle may be determined. Since tables of the values of sin θ (theta), cos θ, and tan θ are available for θ equal to any angle, we make use of this in finding rectangular components of a force.

Suppose we consider a deltoid muscle pulling on the abducted arm with a force of 100 lb. The action line makes an angle of 20 degrees with the humerus (Fig. 6.20). We wish to find the vertical (rotatory) and horizontal (stabilizing) components of this force. If we call the vertical component F_y, and the horizontal component F_x, then

$$F_y = D \sin 20° = 100 \times 0.342 = 34.2 \text{ lb.}$$
$$F_x = D \cos 20° = 100 \times 0.939 = 93.9 \text{ lb.}$$

It may seem strange that the sum of the magnitudes of the two components of the original force is more than the force itself. Recall that it is the square of the hypotenuse of a right triangle which is equal to the sum of the squares of the two sides, or

$$R^2 = F_x{}^2 + F_y{}^2$$

Let us now review the previous examples, which were presented graphically, and supply algebraic solutions. In Figure 6.15C (p. 76) angle $\theta = 45$ degrees and forces T and S are each therefore $0.707 \times B$. If B represents a pull of 10 lb., a force of 7.07 lb. is acting to rotate the part and another force of 7.07 lb. is compressing the elbow joint surfaces. When angle $\theta = 30$ degrees, $T = 0.500 \times 10$, or 5 lb., and $S = 0.866 \times 10$, or 8.66 lb. In Figure 6.16, if the hamstrings pull with a force of 30 lb. on the leg, both the rotational and compressional components, T and S, equal $0.707 \times 30 = 21.2$ lb.

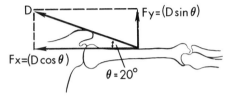

Fig. 6.20. Resolution of deltoid force, D, into rotary component, F_y, and stabilizing component, F_x. Angle of force application, θ, is 20 degrees.

In Figure 6.17, since the weight of the man remains constant, Y is constant in direction and magnitude, and O and X must be obtained from Y. The value of Y for an average man might be 200 lb. In the first figure the force, O, can be obtained from the relation

$$200 = O \cos 20°, \text{ or}$$

$$O = \frac{200}{\cos 20°} = \frac{200}{0.939}$$

$$= 212.9 \text{ lb.}$$

The horizontal component will be

$$X = O \sin 20° = 212.9 \times 0.342 = 72.8 \text{ lb.}$$

With a longer step, as angle θ becomes 30°, the direction and magnitude of the reacting force O changes;

$$O = \frac{200}{\cos 30°} = \frac{200}{0.866} = 230.9 \text{ lb.}$$

and the horizontal component

$$X = O \sin 30° = 230.9 \times 0.5 = 115.4 \text{ lb.}$$

From this it may be seen that with a longer step length, the relative increase in magnitude of the horizontal component X is larger than the increase in the total ground reaction force O. Frictional force at the heel must be much greater when the step is longer than when it is short.

In certain problems we will be interested in only one of the two rectangular components of the original force.

As we saw earlier, the effectiveness of a muscle force or of gravitational pull in rotating a body segment increases as its angle of application to the part approaches 90 degrees. In the case of the biceps acting on the forearm with a force of 10 lb. (Fig. 6.21),

$$T = \sin 15° \times 10 = 0.258 \times 10 = 2.58 \text{ lb.}$$
$$T' = \sin 30° \times 10 = 0.500 \times 10 = 5.00 \text{ lb.}$$
$$T'' = \sin 80° \times 10 = 0.985 \times 10 = 9.85 \text{ lb.}$$

Notice that this is not a linear increase. The rotatory component equals half the original force when the angle at which the force is applied is only 30 degrees. When the angle reaches 45 degrees the rotatory component is 70.7 per cent of the original force, and the rate of increase per unit of joint movement declines toward 90 degrees. These relationships can be seen by reading down the columns of the sine and cosine table.

Analysis of the changing resistance offered by an exercise load on a moving segment will illustrate the pattern of exercise force variation.

1. Problem

An exercise load of 20 lb. is placed on the patient's foot and he extends his knee to exercise the quadriceps muscles (Fig. 6.22).

QUESTION: Find the magnitude of the "exercise force," or force acting at a right angle to the leg at various points in the range of knee extension.

SOLUTION: Using first the *graphic* technique, we may draw line diagrams and find rectangular components of the applied load at selected points in the range of motion. Here we are interested in the rotatory component of the force only. The other component in this case is acting to pull the joint apart.

As the leg hangs vertically, the center of gravity of the leg and the weight is directly below the axis at the knee joint and the action line of the force is in line with the leg. As the knee begins to extend, the action line of the applied load makes ever-increasing angles with the long axis of the leg. We will arbitrarily select knee angles of 0, 30, 60, and 90 degrees to analyze. We choose a scale value representing 20 pounds for our weight vector, and draw a series of line diagrams. Parallelograms are constructed from which the changing values of T can be obtained.

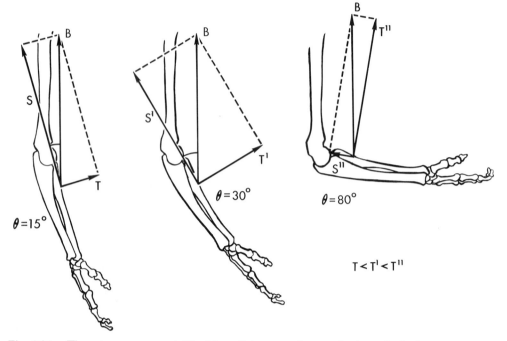

Fig. 6.21. The rotary component, T, of force B increases in magnitude as the body segment moves about its anatomical axis, but this increase is not linear.

From these it is evident that when the leg has moved upward through the first 30 degrees, T has reached half its final maximum value.

We have ignored the weight of the leg itself in this problem. Can you see how its effect should be diagramed throughout this series? Review each characteristic of the force of gravity here to be sure you are visualizing the vector correctly. Add a vector representing leg and foot weight to each of the figures shown and compute its effect in quadriceps resistance exercise.

The *algebraic* method permits us to solve for the "exercise force" or rotatory component of the load by looking up in the table the sine values for the angles of force application. We will select slightly different leg positions this time:

If we had included a knee angle of 45 degrees, where the action line of gravity forms an angle of 45 degrees with the leg axis, we would find that the "exercise force" has increased from zero to over 14 pounds, or about 70 per cent, during

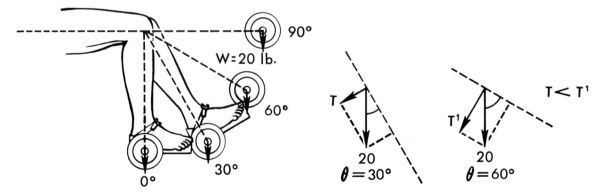

Fig. 6.22. Analysis of "exercise force," or component of total load, W, acting at a right angle to the axis of the leg and opposing knee extension. Four points in the range of motion are shown. Angles of gravitational pull on the leg are indicated for each point. When the leg is vertical, there is no resistance to extension. When the leg is horizontal, the entire load of 20 lb. tends to rotate the leg downward. Rectangular components are shown at 30 and 60 degrees.

ANGLE OF KNEE JOINT	ANGLE OF FORCE APPLICATION	SINE	ROTATORY COMPONENT OF EXERCISE WEIGHT
90°	0°	0.000	0.00 lb.
60	30	0.500	10.00
40	50	0.766	15.32
20	70	0.939	18.78
0	90	1.000	20.00

the first half of the range of knee extension. It increases only 30 per cent during the last half of the range. Of course, the reverse is true as the leg returns from horizontal to vertical. These data are plotted as a solid line in Figure 6.24.

2. Problem

The same approach can be used to analyze another well-known type of resistance exercise—the application of weights through a pulley system. The pulley rope is attached to the patient's heel (Fig. 6.23).

QUESTION: Find the "exercise force" applied through the range of knee extension by a pulley rope supporting a 20 lb. load (i.e., the amount of the total force acting at a right angle to the leg).

SOLUTION: The positions in Figure 6.23 were traced from photographs of a patient performing quadriceps resistance exercises with his knee at 90, 60, 30 and 0 degrees of extension. Angles between the rope and the long axis of the leg were found to be 90, 64, 40 and 19 degrees re-

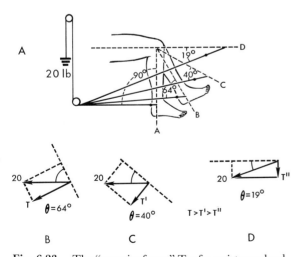

Fig. 6.23. The "exercise force," T, of a resistance load, W (20 lb.), applied through a pulley system is maximum at the beginning of the exercise and decreases as the leg extends through positions A to D.

spectively. By consulting the table, in the algebraic solution of the problem, we find the values of the exercise force to be 20, 17.9, 12.8 and 6.5 lb. at these points in the range of knee extension. These values represent the rotary component of the force in the pulley rope. The data are shown graphically in Figure 6.23.

The pattern of exercise force supplied by a pulley system is quite different from that of a free weight on the foot. The contrast in these resistance patterns may be seen in the curves plotted in Figure 6.24. Maximum force is applied at opposite ends of the range of movement in these two exercise methods, and the rate and magnitude of change in exercise load is less with the pulley system (dotted curve) than with the free weight.

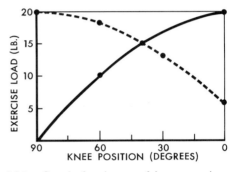

Fig. 6.24. Graph showing quadriceps exercise resistance pattern applied by free weight (solid line) and pulley system (dotted line) through the range of knee extension.

It would appear that the boot method is appropriate if the physical therapist wishes to apply a highly variable load which is maximal when the knee is fully extended. The pulley method provides an exercise force which varies in this case from 100 per cent to 32½ per cent of the exercise weight, and the maximal force is applied when the knee is at right angles.

The next two problems will demonstrate the use of the cosine of the angle of force application.

3. Problem

A paraplegic patient is strengthening his shoulder muscles by means of dumbbell exercises. The arm is abducted to horizontal and the weight is held in the hand. The deltoid is contracting with a force of 227 lb. and its action line forms an angle (ϕ) of 17 degrees with the humerus (Fig. 6.25).

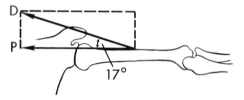

Fig. 6.25. Graphic determination of stabilizing component, P, of deltoid force, D, when the angle of force application is 17 degrees.

QUESTION: What component of the deltoid force is pressing the humeral head against the glenoid cavity?

SOLUTION: Here we need to find the "stabilizing" component of the two rectangular components of the deltoid force. A diagram drawn to scale shows that with such a small angle of incidence of the force, the component P, acting along the humerus, is nearly as large as the original force. With forces of this size the algebraic solution is much more satisfactory than the graphic one and very simple:

$$P = D \cos \phi$$
$$P = 227 \times 0.956$$
$$P = 217 \text{ lb.}$$

4. Problem

As a final example in this section let us return to the Russell traction system shown in Figure 6.12, p. 75. Suppose we wish to determine the force pulling in line with the leg (toward the foot of the bed). Pulley ropes Q and S are applied to the foot and their action lines form angles of 22 and 10 degrees respectively with the long axis of the leg (Fig. 6.26).

QUESTION: Determine the force pulling in line with the leg when 10 lb. of traction weights are applied.

SOLUTION: The graphic solution is shown in the diagram. The tension in each strand of the pulley system is 10 lb. Rectangular components are drawn for Q and S. The component S_x is nearly as large as S, while Q_x is slightly smaller in comparison with Q. Vectors Q_x and S_x are added to obtain R, the resultant force acting in line with the leg. If we have drawn these vectors accurately to scale, the length of R will give us the force value needed in the solution of our problem.

In the algebraic solution we determine from the table that $\cos 10° = 0.985$ and $\cos 22° = 0.927$. Hence the "side adjacent" to the angle of force application in the right triangle in each case has a magnitude of

$$
\begin{aligned}
10 \times 0.985 &= 9.85 \text{ lb. (rope S)} \\
10 \times 0.927 &= \underline{9.27 \text{ lb. (rope Q)}} \\
\text{Total} & 19.12 \text{ lb.}
\end{aligned}
$$

With the pulley arrangement shown, the leg is being pulled along its axis with a force of 19.12 lb. and the structures about the knee joint

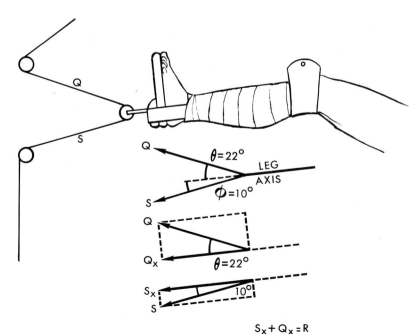

Fig. 6.26. Tension applied to the leg through pulley ropes, Q and S, in Russell traction. Total tension in line with the leg = $Q_x + S_x$, found by taking rectangular components of Q and S.

are pulling back (cephalad) with an equal force.

Examples from the Literature. Diagrams of rectangular components of a force appear frequently in the literature. Often these do not include specific values, but are used to demonstrate by graphic means relative magnitudes of forces which are resolved into component parts. For example, Steindler's kinesiology text[5] has a number of such drawings. In Figure 6.27, the force of the knee flexor muscles (e.g., semitendinosus or sartorius) in the sagittal plane is shown. The rotatory component flexes the leg; the translatory component compresses the knee joint. In the second figure, a vector represents the force of the hip adductor muscle group. This force both adducts the limb and pushes it upward into the acetabulum. The abductor muscle group pushes the femoral head into the acetabulum as well as swinging the leg out to the side.

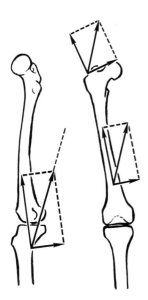

Fig. 6.27. Example of graphical resolution of forces, adapted from Steindler's *Kinesiology*.[5] Muscles represented are the hamstrings, hip abductors, and adductors shown with their respective rectangular components.

Steindler has emphasized the usefulness of the "wasted" or stabilizing components of muscle forces such as these in that they serve to protect the joint structures—capsule and ligaments—from wear and tear. They are also an important factor in postural stability and therefore do not deserve the term "wasted." The magnitude of the stabilizing component is far greater than the rotating component of most muscle forces as the

majority of muscles insert at very small angles to the long axis of the segments.

The method used by A. Fick (p. 11) to determine force components of the hip muscles in the three cardinal planes is explained by the resolution of forces technique. A thigh and pelvis from a cadaver dissection were suspended by Fick in a triangular frame, with the thigh in the anatomical position. The action line of each muscle was estimated from its anatomical location, and was extended until it intersected one or more of the three planes that converged at the axis of the hip joint. The force was then divided "according to the parallelopiped of forces" into its components acting in the respective planes. The action line of an individual muscle was considered to be the resultant of all the small component forces within the muscle, with an equal number of fibers on either side of the line.[6]

As a further example of resolution of a force, Inman et al.[7] observed that the upper part of the trapezius (F) pulls in a diagonal direction on the shoulder, providing both a supportive component, F_y, and an adductory component, F_x (Fig. 6.28). From observations of shoulder function these authors concluded that:

"Owing to the changes in position of the scapula during elevation, the resultant of the supportive and rotary components supplied by the upper portion of the trapezius . . . fluctuate(s) in its angle of action. This fluctuation reveals an interesting mechanism in the action of the trapezius. In the resting position, the muscle is entirely supportive. With the first 35 degrees of (arm) elevation, the angle of action of the muscle changes, so

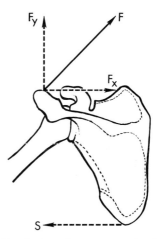

Fig. 6.28. Resolution of upper trapezius force, F, into supporting component, F_y, and adductory component, F_x. Abductor force, S, of serratus anterior muscle is shown below. (Based on Inman et al.[7])

that its force is equally divided between the supportive and rotary roles. From 35 to 140 degrees, the muscle is increasingly more effective as a rotator, with its maximum power at 90 degrees, and beyond 140 degrees its rotary efficiency decreases and its supportive rises. This complicated mechanism of action of the upper trapezius is achieved by simple elevation of the shoulder girdle as a whole."[7]

An interesting application of resolving a force has been made by Rose and Wallace[8] in an analysis of typical hand deformity resulting from arthritis. In accounting for the characteristic ulnar deviation of the fingers, these authors review the general scheme of dorsal interosseus muscle action on the fingers. The mechanics of the first dorsal interosseus muscle is then considered, wherein fibers converge to act on a centrally located tendon (Fig. 6.29A).

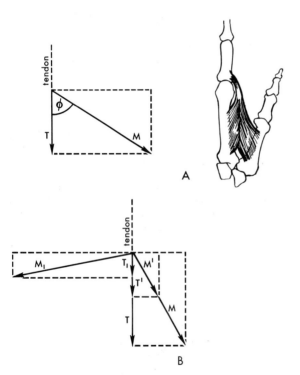

Fig. 6.29.   Relation of tendon shortening to muscle contraction in pennate fiber arrangement. Fiber M contracts with force T in the direction of the central tendon. In B, Rose and Wallace[8] have applied this concept in analyzing typical hand deformity in arthritis, where:
M = normal fiber of first dorsal interosseus muscle
M' = force of fiber weakened by disuse
M_1 = force of opposing fiber, after adaptive changes
T = force exerted by normal fiber along tendon
T' = force exerted by M' in direction of tendon
T_1 = force of M_1 in direction of tendon.

According to the description given, M represents the force of a muscle fiber, and if the angle ϕ at which the fibers approach the tendon is 60 degrees, cos ϕ is 0.500 and thus T, the component of M acting in the direction of the central tendon, is ½M. If the angle ϕ increases, the component T will decrease and vice versa. This analysis can be applied to any bipennate or unipennate arrangement of muscle fibers. The authors go on to point out that in arthritic hand deformities the intrinsic muscles become weakened from disuse. (Fig. 6.29B). The index finger becomes deviated ulnarward and fiber M, although having a more acute angle of insertion into the central tendon, becomes further weakened from constant stretch. The opposing fiber, M_1, shortens adaptively. Thus M_1 has a poor angle of insertion. "Any corrective exercise must balance the bipennate components, yet keep the forces acting in the direction of the tendon as large as possible."[8]

Moments of Forces.   So far we have discussed composition and resolution of forces for the purpose of determining a single resultant force from two or more original forces, or of resolving an original force into components. We may need to go a step farther and compute moments of forces in certain types of problems. Consideration of such a problem shows that after rectangular components of an obliquely applied force are determined we can proceed as with a parallel force system.

5. Problem

In a discussion of manual muscle testing, Brunnstrom[9] considers the difference in quadriceps force required to support the leg when it is (1) in a horizontal position, and (2) at 30 degrees from horizontal (Fig. 6.30). In her example the leg is considered to weigh 5 lb. and its center of gravity to lie 8 in. below the knee axis. The patellar tendon inserts 2 in. below the knee axis and its action line forms an angle of 30 degrees with the long axis of the leg.

QUESTION: What tension must the quadriceps exert to keep the leg fully extended against gravitational force in the two positions described?

SOLUTION: Since the leg is known to be at rest, we can use the equations of equilibrium. The term for the rectangular component of Q acting at right angles to the leg is Q sin θ.

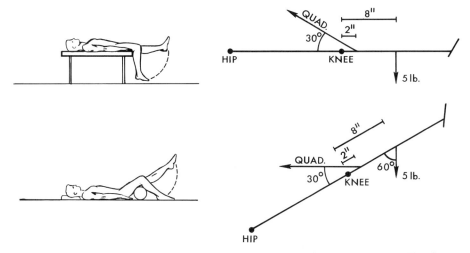

Fig. 6.30. Comparison of two possible muscle testing positions for the quadriceps. The force necessary to maintain the knee in extension is greater in the upper figure, as the pull of gravity is fully effective in rotation. (From Brunnstrom.[9])

Clockwise moments will be $+$. With the leg in a horizontal position,

$$(8 \times 5) - (Q \sin 30° \times 2) = 0$$
$$40 - Q \times 0.500 \times 2 = 0$$
$$Q = 40 \text{ lb.}$$

With the leg in a position 30 degrees from horizontal, we must find the rotational component of gravitational force as well as that of the quadriceps force:

$$(5 \sin 60° \times 8) - (Q \sin 30° \times 2) = 0$$
$$5 \times 0.866 \times 8 - Q \times 0.500 \times 2 = 0$$
$$Q = 34.64 \text{ lb.}$$

Thus more quadriceps tension is required in the first case, where gravitational force is applied to the leg at a right angle.

6. Problem

The paraplegic patient in problem 3, p. 81, contracted his deltoid with a force of 227 lb. in order to support the dumbbell in his hand. Let us say the deltoid tubercle was 5 in. from the shoulder axis and the exercise weight in the hand was 22 in. from the shoulder axis. The angle of force application of the muscle was 17°.

QUESTION: How much did the dumbbell weigh?

SOLUTION: If clockwise moments are $+$,

$$W \times 22 = 227 \sin 17° \times 5$$
$$22W = 227 \times 0.956 \times 5$$
$$W = 15 \text{ lb.}$$

7. Problem

A patient lifts a deLorme boot with weights through the range of knee extension (Fig. 6.31). The boot, bar and weights total 34 lb. Here the action line of the quadriceps intersects the long axis of the leg 4 in. distal to the tibial articular surface at the knee and forms an angle of 20 degrees with the leg. The center of gravity of the boot, bar and exercise weights combined is 24 in. distal to the knee joint (tibial surface).

QUESTION: What is the pressure against the articular surfaces of the knee joint resulting from muscle tension when the leg is (1) in full extension; (2) flexed to 45 degrees (half way to extension)?

SOLUTION: Taking rectangular components of Q, representing quadriceps force, we see that:

$$T = Q \sin 20°, \text{ and}$$
$$S = Q \cos 20° \text{ (compression force).}$$

In order to determine the magnitude of S we must first find Q. Since we do not need to know the value of T, we can use it only in relation to the term for Q: $T = Q \sin 20°$. We now have the terms of a parallel force system and we can proceed as before. With the leg fully extended, clockwise moments $+$,

$$(34 \times 24) - (T \times 4) = 0$$
$$(34 \times 24) - (Q \sin 20° \times 4) = 0$$
$$816 - (Q \times 0.342 \times 4) = 0$$
$$816 = 1.37Q$$
$$Q = 596.5 \text{ lb.}$$

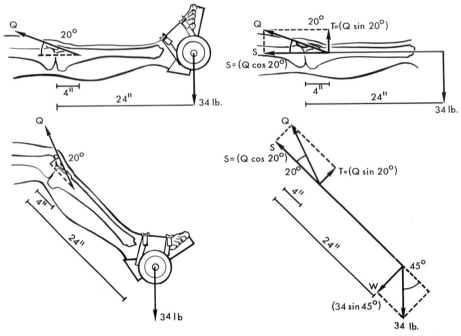

Fig. 6.31. Pressure on the knee joint in quadriceps resistance exercise at two positions in the range of knee extension. Q = quadriceps force; T = rotary component of quadriceps; W = rotary component of the exercise weight, which is 34 lb. The angle of force application of the quadriceps on the tibia is considered to be 20 degrees in each case.

The compression force, $Q \cos 20°$, is then $596.5 \times 0.939 = 560.1$ lb.

With the leg at an angle of 45 degrees, the computation again becomes a little more complicated. We must find the rotational component of the exercise force as well as that of the quadriceps muscle pull.

$$(34 \sin 45° \times 24) -$$
$$(Q \sin 20° \times 4) = 0$$
$$576.9 = Q \times 1.368$$
$$Q = 421.7 \text{ lb.}$$

The component of the quadriceps force which is pressing the articular surfaces of the knee together is $Q \cos 20°$ or $421.7 \times 0.939 = 395.9$ lb. when the leg is half way to full extension in this exercise. The quadriceps force is actually slightly greater than the value shown when the leg is moving upward.

Alternate Method of Determining Moments

As we saw in Chapter 5, the moment of a force may also be found by multiplying the total force by the perpendicular distance from its action line to the moment center (Fig. 6.32). This product will be the same as that obtained by taking the rotary component and multiplying by the perpendicular distance from its action line to the moment center.

The choice of method in finding moments is a matter of convenience. For example, in Figure 6.32 it would be difficult to measure accurately

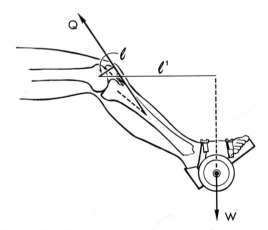

Fig. 6.32. Alternate method of computing moments which does not involve finding rectangular components. $Q \times l$ = moment of quadriceps muscle; $W \times l'$ = moment of exercise load, W. These products (W × l' and Q × l) will be exactly the same as the corresponding moments in Figure 6.31, T × 4 in. (quadriceps) and W × 24 in. (exercise load).

distances *l* and *l'*, and the method used in problem 7 would be preferable.

Replacing vectors by equivalent components enables us to change the force diagram to a form which will permit a solution to problems. This procedure is necessary in the approach to concurrent and general force systems to be considered in the next chapter.

Graphic Determination of the Resultant of a Parallel Force System

With an understanding of resolution of forces, we can now find the resultant of a parallel force system by graphic means, which was omitted in the previous chapter. The procedure is similar to

that for the linear system, but it becomes a little more involved.

Two steps are needed: First we find the magnitude and direction of the resultant force, exactly as in the linear system. Next we locate the position of its action line by resolving each force in the system into components. For example, given three forces of 5, 10 and 15 lb. at distances shown in Figure 6.33, find the resultant force. To determine its magnitude and direction, we draw a vector diagram of the forces as in the linear system. All are placed in the same straight line, tacking the beginning of one onto the end of the preceding one. A line from the beginning of the first vector to the end of the last gives the magnitude and direction of the resultant.

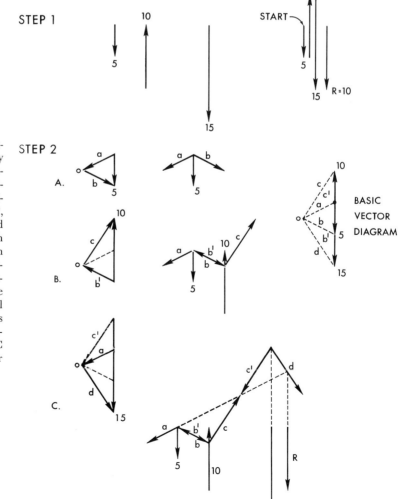

Fig. 6.33. Finding the resultant in a parallel force system by graphic means. In step 1, a vector diagram is drawn to determine the direction and magnitude of the resultant. In step 2, each original force is replaced by equivalent vectors which are drawn on the line diagram of the force system. The intersection of the first and last vector is on the action line of the resultant force (see text). All the information necessary is given in the "basic vector diagram," but steps A, B, and C are shown separately in order to clarify the procedure.

To find the position of the action line of the resultant, we replace each force by component vectors. We know that the components of any force must intersect on the action line of the original force, and that they must form two sides of a triangle with the original force being the third side. Starting with the 5 lb. force in the vector diagram, we draw two lines using it as a base to construct a triangle (Fig. 6.33*A*). These two lines (a, b) represent components replacing the original force and they must be moved parallel to their position to make them intersect on the action line of the 5 lb. force in the vector diagram.

We now repeat the process, dividing the 10 lb. force into two components (Fig. 6.33*B*). This time, however, we will specify that the first component, b′ must be equal, opposite, and coincident with the second component, b, of the first force. When the second pair of components (b′, c) is transferred to intersect on the action line of the original 10 lb. force, we see that one of them (b′) cancels component b of the previous force.

This process is repeated until all the forces have been replaced by components. In our problem, the first component of the 15 lb. force, c′, is made to cancel component c of the 10 lb. force. We now discover that all the components have cancelled each other with the exception of the first and last one. Therefore these two com-

ponents, a and d, represent the resultant of the entire system and they must intersect on the action line of the resultant. To find this juncture, the action line of one or both vectors may be extended.

Since we have already determined the magnitude and direction of the resultant, all we needed was the point of intersection of the first and last components to give us the proper position of the action line of the resultant of the force system. It is convenient simply to transfer the direction of the action lines from the vector diagram where they were constructed to their proper positions on the forces in the space diagram. Each step in the procedure has been shown separately in Figure 6.33.

For further examples, let us return to two problems solved previously by the algebraic method so that the solutions may be compared.

1. Problem

On page 48 in problem number 3, an exercise weight of 30 lb. was placed on the foot. The patient's leg and foot weighed 9 lb., and distances were as shown in Figure 6.34.

QUESTION: Find the resultant force of segment weight and exercise load.

SOLUTION: A vector diagram is constructed, and the magnitude and direction of R determined. Next, components a and b are drawn from point o to represent the 9 lb. force, and b′ and c, the 30 lb. force. (Point o may be located at any convenient place.) These components are transferred to the space diagram and the action line of the resultant force located at the intersection of vectors a and c.

2. Problem

On p. 47, problem number 1 involved a force system of 32, 12, and 24 lb. with distances as shown in Figure 6.35.

QUESTION: Find the resultant force of the system.

SOLUTION: As before, we draw a vector diagram, resolve the original vectors into components, and place the components on a space diagram to find the intersection of the first and last component vectors. We now have the magnitude, direction, and action line of the resultant force and can put it in its proper position in the original line diagram.

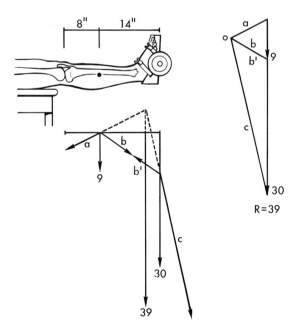

Fig. 6.34. Graphic determination of the resultant of the parallel force system in problem 3, p. 48.

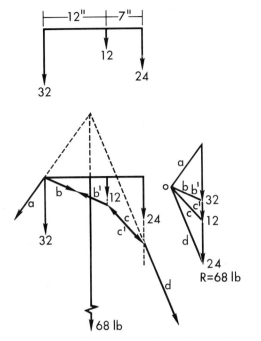

Fig. 6.35. Graphic determination of the resultant of the parallel force system in problem 1, p. 47.

You may wish to repeat the three solutions discussed in this section, giving the forces in each problem different components from those selected here. This should not, of course, affect the answer.

There is the possibility that the resultant of a parallel force system may be a couple. In this case the vector diagram will close. When the components of the forces are transferred to the original system, the first and last component will be equal in magnitude and parallel to each other instead of intersecting. The magnitude of the couple will be the product of one of these components and the distance between them.

Graphical Solution to the Equilibrium Problem

The same procedure is used as in locating the position of the resultant force in the parallel force system. The magnitude and direction of the unknown force is obtained by making the vector diagram close. The final vector is placed so that it passes from the tip of the last known vector to the beginning of the first vector in the diagram. Its position is determined by the point of intersection of the first and last component vectors in the space diagram.

Questions

1. Mention an example of composition of forces in body movement which has not already been suggested; an example of resolution of forces.

2. A 200-lb. patient referred to your clinic for posture exercises has difficulty in keeping his lumbar spine flat while doing a straight leg raising exercise (supine). Make line diagrams of the lower limb (1) with one hip flexed 20 degrees; (2) 75 degrees. Add vectors representing gravitational pull on the limb and show rectangular components in each case. What is the magnitude of the rotational component ("exercise force") in each case as determined by the algebraic method? In which exercise position would the lumbar spine be most likely to hyperextend? Explain. Compare pressure on the hip joint surfaces in the two positions of the limb caused by gravitational force.

3. A paraplegia patient strengthens his shoulders by raising a 15 lb. dumbbell to shoulder level with his arm straight.

(a) Find the effective "exercise force" (rotatory component of gravitational pull on the weight) when the arm is abducted 40 degrees from the side of the trunk.

(b) Find the force in the deltoid muscle necessary to maintain the arm in a horizontal position. (Consider the angle of deltoid force application on the arm to be 20 degrees, and estimate the distances you need in solving the problem.)

4. Diagram and determine algebraically the rotatory component of the semimembranosus muscle at the knee when the muscle pulls with a force of 50 lb. and the knee is flexed to 10 degrees; to 45 degrees. What is the pressure on the joint structures between the femur and tibia in each case?

5. (a) Diagram the rotational component of gravitational force acting on the head, trunk and arms (considered as a unit) during a "sit-up" exercise when the patient's trunk is halfway to vertical and (1) the arms are at the sides; (2) the arms are overhead.

(b) Estimate distances you need and determine the moment exerted about the hip joints by gravitational force on the trunk in 5a (1) and (2). Explain why these moments differ, but the rotational components do not differ.

6. Repeat the computations in problem number 7 adding the weight of the leg and foot (9.5 lb.). The center of gravity of these segments is 8.5 in. distal to the knee joint.

7. Progressive resistive exercise loads for the quadriceps of 90 lb. have been achieved by Klein,[10] using young men as subjects. On the basis of the measurements in problem number 7, find the quadriceps force and the articular compression force in the knee in full extension when an exercise load of 90 lb. is used.

Bibliography

1. Flitter, H. H.: *An Introduction to Physics in Nursing.* St. Louis, C. V. Mosby Co., 1948, p. 22.
2. Braus, H.: *Anatomie des Menschen.* Berlin, Springer Verlag, 1954, p. 360.
3. Calderwood, C.: Russell traction. *Amer. J. Nursing, 43*:1–6, 1943.
4. Inman, V. T.: Functional aspects of the abductor muscles of the hip, *J. Bone Joint Surg. (Amer.), 29*:607–619, 1947, p. 615.
5. Steindler, A.: *Kinesiology.* Springfield, Ill.: Charles C Thomas Co., 1955, p. 286.
6. Fick, A.: Statische Berachtung der Muskulature des Oberschankels. *Zeitschrift für Rationelle Medicin, 9*:94–106, 1850.
7. Inman, V. T., Saunders, J. B., and Abbott, L. C.: The function of the shoulder joint. *J. Bone Joint Surg. (Amer.), 26*:1–30, 1944.
8. Rose, D. L., and Wallace, L. I.: A remedial occupational therapy program for the residuals of rheumatoid arthritis of the hand. *Amer. J. Phys. Med., 31*:5–13, 1952.
9. Brunnstrom, S.: Muscle group testing. *Physio. Rev., 21*:3–22, 1941.
10. Klein, K.: Progressive resistive exercise and its utilization in the recovery period following knee injury. *Brit. J. Phys. Med., 20*:85–92.

CHAPTER SEVEN

Concurrent and General Force Systems

When the infinite variety of postures of the human body is considered, along with the complexity of arrangement of the bones and muscles within the body, it is apparent that analysis of many problems in biomechanics will involve forces that are neither parallel nor linear. We have already seen in Chapter 6 how concurrent arrangements of forces can be simplified for analysis. We now have the basic technique for solving more extensive problems involving equilibrium of the entire body or finding a single resultant force representing several forces acting in various positions.

An endless number of problems can now be attacked. In some situations, for example in traction systems and application of exercise apparatus, the magnitude and direction of forces are not difficult to determine. In the case of forces within the body, however, vector characteristics of muscle tension, segment mass, and center of gravity positions must be estimated. Such estimates are made more accurate by the use of force plate studies, dynamometer tests, photographs and moving pictures, x-ray films and cineradiography, and electronic monitoring devices designed to record displacements objectively.

The present text is primarily concerned with techniques of analysis. As instrumentation improves and more accurate and complete data become available on morphological and physiological parameters of the human body, analysis of biomechanical problems will become more refined. Meanwhile the techniques of analysis will be useful in making gross estimates of forces with an acceptable degree of accuracy.

An important area which has been relatively unexplored is calculation of forces on joint surfaces in the body. With increased interest in arthritis and the collagen diseases, and with degeneration of articular cartilage associated with the aging process, the physician and therapist should be aware of joint pressure "dosages" resulting from various postural positions and types of therapeutic exercise. For example, the quadriceps may be exercised by active knee extension with the patient seated, by addition of deLorme or pulley weights, by stair climbing and similar activities, or by deep knee-bending exercises. How does compression of the knee joint vary with these activities, and at different positions of the joint from flexion to extension? What magnitudes of pressure at the knee are involved in rising from a chair and being seated? As further examples, how does pressure on the first cervical vertebra change when the head is moved from an upright position into full flexion, as in looking at the floor? How does the load on the femoral head vary with body positions and with added loads carried in the hand?

It must be remembered that when we select static positions for analysis, we are only approximating the precise forces accompanying actual movement. Analysis by this means ignores accelerations, momentum, and frictional effects which require the techniques of dynamics for analysis. However, the conditions under which very slow deliberate movements common in therapeutic exercise are carried out resemble those of static postures. Thus analysis of a series of selected positions will give an approximation of required muscle tension and articular pressures.

Investigation of the magnitude of individual muscle forces required to sustain various postural positions is made difficult by the complex arrangement of muscle groups within the body. While there are a few joint movements controlled by a single tendon (knee extension, flex-ion of distal phalanges of digits), most joints have several muscles controlling them in each direction of motion. Approximations of the effect of component muscles in a group can be made based on their cross sectional area and their relative positions in relation to the joint. Electromyographic studies provide interesting data on phasic activity of muscle, but action potential recordings are not satisfactory for indicating definitive force data.

It was stated in Chapter 1 that an understanding of the material presented in this text would help the reader to interpret the literature relating to biomechanics and kinesiology. Perhaps the ultimate test of the usefulness of the material to the student will be his ability to set up problems and to solve them for himself. Before going on, let us review some basic points in procedure.

Depending on the known values of the problem, one of two techniques will be involved: finding a resultant or solving the equilibrium problem. If an object is not at rest, the forces acting on it may be analyzed with the purpose of reducing the force system to its simplest form. The resultant may be a force or, in the case of a parallel or general force system, a couple. In the graphic solution, a vector diagram is drawn. The resultant is represented by a vector passing from the tail of the first to the tip of the last vector in the diagram. If the force system is in equilibrium, on the other hand, the final vector must close the force polygon, passing from the tip of the last to the tail of the first vector.

When the object is known to be at rest, the equations of equilibrium may be applied. In this case one, two, or three unknown values may be determined, depending on the type of force system involved. Facility with the free body diagram is essential. Steps in the solution of the equilibrium problem are as follows:

1. Selection of the free body appropriate to the solution of the problem.

2. Drawing of the free body diagram.

3. Determination of the type of force system involved and choosing of coordinate axes and moment centers.

4. Substituting the forces from the free body diagram into the pertinent equations of equilibrium.

5. Solving the equations of equilibrium to obtain the unknown values.

In the free body diagram, forces must be

shown acting at all points where the free body makes contact with another member. These forces must be represented as vectors, showing their direction, and letters are assigned to them to represent their magnitudes. If we are to arrive at the correct solution, all forces pertinent to the problem must be included and none that are not involved may be included. After the free body diagram has been completed, we examine the force system to see which class is represented, and whether the system exists in a single plane or in space. (In this text we deal only with forces in a plane.)

Concurrent Force Systems

A home traction device similar to one described in the literature is shown in Figure 7.1A. A cervical traction head sling is supported by two vertical strands passing over pulleys, with a third strand making an angle of 45 degrees with the horizontal. When a traction weight of two pounds is applied to the system, what is the force applied to the head? An examination of the forces involved in this problem indicates that they are neither linear nor parallel, but meet at a point. This type of force system is called concurrent and before we can solve this problem it will be necessary to learn what equations are required to define the resultant of such a system. Many examples of concurrent arrangement of

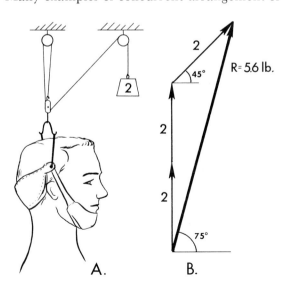

forces are found in exercise and traction apparatus as well as in musculoskeletal function.

Resultants. To find the resultant of a concurrent force system by the algebraic method, it is necessary to use the technique of breaking up each force into rectangular components, that is, to replace the original by two forces that are at right angles to each other. We select a direction for the X and Y axes and then take each force in turn and replace it by its X and Y components. After all the forces have been replaced by components lying along the X and Y axes, the system has been reduced to two linear systems which are at right angles to each other, an arrangement with which we are already familiar.

As we learned earlier, the X component is obtained by multiplying the force by the cosine of the angle that the force makes with the X axis. In like manner, the Y component is determined by multiplying the force by the sine of the same angle. Care must be taken to determine the proper algebraic sign for each of these components: those going up and to the right are positive, and those going down and to the left are negative.

When the system has been reduced to two resultant forces, one in the X direction and one in the Y direction, we find the single force which is equivalent to these two rectangular components.

To illustrate the procedure, suppose we have three forces of 120, 100, and 50 lb., as shown in Figure 7.2A. We construct the X and Y axes and proceed to replace each force by rectangular components. Beginning with the horizontal components,

$$R_x = \Sigma F_x = \Sigma F \cos \theta$$
$$= 100 \cos 30° + 50 \cos 45° - 120 \cos 60°$$
$$= 100 \times 0.866 + 50 \times 0.707 - 120 \times 0.500$$
$$= 86.6 + 35.3 - 60$$
$$R_x = 61.9 \text{ (to the right)}$$

To determine components along the Y axes,

$$R_y = \Sigma F_y = \Sigma F \sin \theta$$
$$= 100 \sin 30° - 50 \sin 45° + 120 \sin 60°$$
$$= 50 - 35.3 + 103.9$$
$$R_y = 118.6 \text{ (upward)}$$

The single force which is the resultant of these two rectangular components is the hypotenuse

Fig. 7.1. Cervical neck traction apparatus described in problem 1; graphic determination of resultant force.

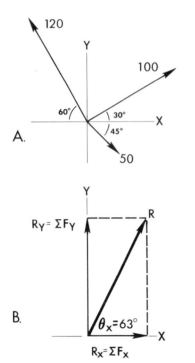

Fig. 7.2. Vector diagram for algebraic determination of resultant of concurrent force system.

of the triangle of which the values R_x and R_y are the sides.

Then,

$$R = \sqrt{R_x^2 + R_y^2} = \sqrt{\Sigma F_x^2 + \Sigma F_y^2}$$

and the angle the resultant makes with the horizontal will be obtained from,

$$\sin \theta_x = \frac{\Sigma F_y}{R} \text{ or } \cos \theta_x = \frac{\Sigma F_x}{R}$$

Thus, in the present problem,

$$R = \sqrt{61.9^2 + 118.6^2}$$
$$= 133 \text{ lb.}$$
$$\sin \theta_x = \frac{118.6}{133}$$
$$= 0.892$$

Consulting the table of sines we find that 0.892 is the sine of approximately 63 degrees. We cannot determine from the angle alone whether the force is directed upward or downward from the X axis, or to the right or left. We draw a diagram of ΣF_y and ΣF_x in their proper directions according to their signs, and the direction of the force is given by the diagonal as shown in Figure 7.2B.

In the *graphic* solution, lines representing the

forces are drawn in order, with the tail of one touching the tip of the preceding one (Fig. 7.3). The resultant will be the line drawn from the *tail* of the first to the *tip* of the last. The resultant force must pass through the point of concurrence where the original forces of the system meet. In this way the resultant force is completely defined.

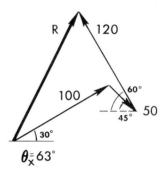

Fig. 7.3. Graphic solution for resultant of concurrent force system shown in Figure 7.2.

1. Problem

Now let us return to the cervical traction device described earlier, which has two vertical and one 45 degree strands carrying a traction weight of 2 lbs. (Fig. 7.1).

QUESTION: Find the resultant force applied to the head by the three supporting strands.

SOLUTION: In setting up the X and Y axes we find that two of the strands coincide with the Y axes and the third makes an angle of 45 degrees with it.

$$R_x = \Sigma F_x = \Sigma F \cos \theta$$
$$= 2 \cos \theta$$
$$= 2 \times 0.707$$
$$R_x = 1.41 \text{ lb.}$$
$$R_y = \Sigma F_y = \Sigma F \sin \theta$$
$$= 2 + 2 + (2 \times 0.707)$$
$$R_y = 5.41 \text{ lb.}$$
$$R = \sqrt{1.41^2 + 5.41^2}$$
$$= 5.6 \text{ lb.}$$
$$\sin \theta_x = \frac{\Sigma F_y}{R} = \frac{5.41}{5.6}$$
$$= 0.966$$
$$\theta_x = 75°$$

The resultant force of 5.6 lb. pulls upward and forward on the patient's head, its action line forming an angle of 75 degrees with the horizontal. The graphic solution is shown in Figure 7.1B.

An action line of traction force slightly forward of vertical is often used clinically to increase stretch on the posterior neck structures, as was mentioned earlier. In the original article from which this illustration was adapted,[1] three vertical strands were used and the fourth made an angle of 60 degrees with the horizontal, rather than 45 degrees. How would the resultant force applied by a 2 lb. weight be altered under these circumstances?

2. Problem

In a traction system three 10 lb. forces are applied to the femur as shown in Figure 7.4.

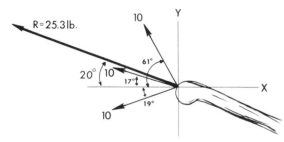

Fig. 7.4. Resultant of traction system applied to femur.

QUESTION: Find the resultant force acting on the femur.

SOLUTION: Beginning with the horizontal components,

$R_x = \Sigma F_x$
$\quad = \Sigma F \cos \theta$
$\quad = -10 \cos 61° - 10 \cos 17° - 10 \cos 19°$
$\quad = -10 \times 0.485 - 10 \times 0.956 - 10 \times 0.946$
$\quad = -23.9$ lb. (to the left)
$R_y = \Sigma F_y$
$\quad = \Sigma F \sin \theta$
$\quad = 10 \sin 61° + 10 \sin 17° - 10 \sin 19°$
$\quad = 10 \times 0.875 + 10 \times 0.292 - 10 \times 0.326$
$\quad = 8.41$ lb. (upward)
$R = \sqrt{23.9^2 + 8.41^2}$
$\quad = 25.3$ lb.
$\sin \theta_x = \dfrac{\Sigma F_y}{R} = \dfrac{8.4}{25.3} = 0.332$
$$\theta_x = 19°$$

The angle formed between the resultant and the horizontal is between 19 and 20 degrees, and a diagram of forces F_y (upward) and F_x (to the left) gives the direction of R. This force is found to be in line with the femur. (Later we will add the weight of the leg and foot to this problem.)

The foregoing examples illustrate analysis of traction arrangements and exercise and assistive apparatus found in the clinic. When the technique followed here is used to analyze arrangements of muscle and joint forces in the body, some assumptions must be made regarding the magnitudes of the forces and their exact anatomical location.

3. Problem

Let us return to the case of the three hip abductor muscles controlling the pelvis in the frontal plane (Fig. 7.5). We will assign force values of 10, 40, and 20 lb. on the basis of Inman's estimate of relative mass of the tensor fasciae latae, gluteus medius and minimus muscles.[2] The action lines of these muscles are estimated to make angles with the horizontal of 86, 78, and 48 degrees respectively, acting downward and lateralward.

QUESTION: Find the resultant force in the frontal plane of the three hip abductor muscles.

SOLUTION: Beginning with the horizontal components:

$R_x = \Sigma F_x$
$\quad = \Sigma F \cos \theta$
$\quad = -10 \cos 86° - 20 \cos 48° - 40 \cos 78°$
$\quad = -0.7 - 13.4 - 8.32$
$\quad = -22.4$ lb. (to the left)
$R_y = \Sigma F_y$
$\quad = \Sigma F \sin \theta$
$\quad = -20 \sin 48° - 40 \sin 78° - 10 \sin 86°$
$\quad = -14.86 - 39.12 - 9.98$
$\quad = -64.0$ lb. (downward)
$R = \sqrt{22.4^2 + 64.0^2}$
$\quad = 67.7$ lb.
$\sin \theta_x = \dfrac{F_y}{R} = \dfrac{64.0}{67.7}$
$\quad = 0.945$
$$\theta_x = 71°$$

The resultant force on the pelvis is 67.7 lb. and it acts downward to the left at an angle of 71 degrees to the horizontal.

The graphic solution is more direct than the algebraic solution in obtaining the resultant of a concurrent system of forces. It fundamentally makes use of the triangle law, but only a part of each triangle need be represented in the construction of the vector diagram. Constructing the third side, or resultant of each two forces in

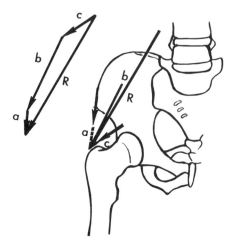

Fig. 7.5. Resultant force of three hip abductor muscles controlling the pelvis in the frontal plane. (Redrawn from Inman.[2])

turn, is unnecessary and a vector diagram of the original forces is adequate. The position of the action line of the resultant is easily determined since it must pass through the point of concurrence of the system. The graphic solution, which is very simple, should be used to check the algebraic solution as before.

The Equilibrium Problem. Before we can solve problems involving equilibrium of concurrent force systems we must examine the conditions which are necessary and sufficient to define equilibrium for this system. The procedure for defining equilibrium of a force system of this type is to make the resultants in the horizontal and vertical directions vanish. The two equations* needed to satisfy these conditions are:

$$\Sigma F_x = 0$$
$$\Sigma F_y = 0$$

Note that in this case there is no possibility of a resultant couple. If a resultant of a concurrent force system exists it must be a single force.

In the algebraic solution, substituting in the equation $\Sigma F_x = 0$, we take each force in turn and obtain its X component by multiplying the force by the cosine of the angle that its action line makes with the horizontal axis. As before, all forces tending to go upward and to the right will have positive components, and all forces tending to go to the left and downward will have negative components. Since we have two independent equations, any two unknowns may be determined, such as the magnitude and direc-

tion of one force or the magnitude of two forces whose directions are known. Each of these unknowns is assigned a letter or symbol and must be included in the equation.

4. Problem

A simple example of a concurrent force system in equilibrium involves forces about the ankle joint in standing. The subject in Figure 7.6 weighs 157 lb.; if the weight of the feet is subtracted, W = 153 lb. The action line of gravity, W, on the body falls anterior to the ankle axis. Therefore tension is necessary in the calf muscles to prevent the body from swaying forward over the toes.

QUESTION: What is the magnitude of tension, T, necessary in the calf muscles to control anterior body sway in the position shown, and

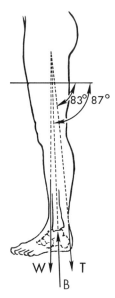

Fig. 7.6. Forces acting at the ankle joint to support the body in relaxed standing: W = body weight; T = tension in the calf muscles, acting as a guy rope; B = force at the tibio-talar joint.

* Two other sets of equations may be used to define equilibrium of the concurrent system. They are:

$$\Sigma F_x = 0$$
$$\Sigma M_A = 0 \text{ where point A cannot be chosen on the Y axis,}$$

and

$$\Sigma M_A = 0$$
$$\Sigma M_B = 0 \text{ where a line joining points A and B cannot pass through the point of concurrence.}$$

what compression force acts between the talus and tibia as a result of body weight and muscle tension?

SOLUTION: The accompanying line diagram was drawn from a photograph in which the action line of gravity was determined by the board and scale method described earlier (p. 58). Action lines of the tendo-Achilles muscle group force, T, and tibio-talar joint force, B, have been assumed from anatomical relationships. B is found to form an angle of 87 degrees with the horizontal, and T, an angle of 83 degrees with the horizontal. Then,

$$\Sigma F_x = -B \cos 87° + T \cos 83° = 0$$
$$\Sigma F_y = B \sin 87° - T \sin 83° - W = 0$$

(from ΣF_x) $\quad B = \dfrac{T \cos 83°}{\cos 87°}$

(from ΣF_y, substituting the equivalent term for B)

$$\frac{T \cos 83°}{\cos 87°} \sin 87° - T \sin 83° = W$$

$$T \left(\frac{\cos 83°}{\cos 87°} \sin 87° - \sin 83° \right) = W$$

$$T = \frac{W}{\left(\dfrac{0.122}{0.052} 0.999 - 0.993 \right)} = \frac{153}{1.35}$$

$$T = 113.3 \text{ lb.}$$

$$B = \frac{113.3 \, (0.122)}{0.052}$$

$$B = 265.8 \text{ lb.}$$

According to this analysis, the calf muscles must exert a total tension of 113.3 lb. to stabilize the body in the upright position, or about 57 lb. on each side. The supra-talar compression force is approximately 133 lb. on each side.

Joseph[3] has estimated the unilateral tension required in the calf muscles in relaxed standing to be about 35 lb. The present figures agree more closely with those of Smith,[4] who estimated that the force in these muscles in standing varied from 59 to 178 lb. on each side. The figure would vary according to the degree of anterior sway of the body over the feet.

In concurrent force analyses with the body segments in equilibrium, the vector passing through the point of contact at the joint involved will include the effect of stabilizing forces of muscles and ligaments in the compression of articular surfaces. This vector is equal and opposite to the resultant of all the forces acting about the joint which are necessary for equilibrium. The next two examples will illustrate this point.

5. Problem

A medical student whose head weighs 10.5 lb. is looking into a microscope (Fig. 7.7).

QUESTION: What tension must the neck extensor muscles exert to support the head in this position, and what is the compression force on the first cervical vertebra?

SOLUTION: We construct a free body diagram of the head, putting in the vectors W and M to represent the gravitational and head extensor muscle forces respectively. Since equilibrium exists and three forces in equilibrium must be concurrent (or parallel), a third force must pass between the atlanto-occipital joint and the point of concurrence of forces W and M. We will call this force B and its action line is found to make an angle ϕ of 60 degrees with the horizontal. M makes an angle θ of 33 degrees with the horizontal.

Filling in our equations of equilibrium, we have

$$\Sigma F_x = -B \cos \phi + M \cos \theta = 0$$
$$\Sigma F_y = B \sin \phi - M \sin \theta - W = 0$$

(from $\Sigma F_x = 0$) $\quad B = \dfrac{M \cos \theta}{\cos \phi}$

(from $\Sigma F_y = 0$)

$$M \frac{\cos \theta}{\cos \phi} \sin \phi - M \sin \theta = W$$

$$M \left(\frac{\cos \theta}{\cos \phi} \sin \phi - \sin \theta \right) = W$$

$$M = \frac{W}{\left(\dfrac{\cos \theta}{\cos \phi} \sin \phi - \sin \theta \right)}$$

$$= \frac{10.5}{\left(\dfrac{0.839}{0.500} 0.866 - 0.545 \right)}$$

$$M = 11.6 \text{ lb.}$$

Now we can solve for B:

$$B = \frac{11.6 \, (0.839)}{0.500} = \frac{9.7324}{0.5}$$

$$B = 19.5 \text{ lb.}$$

The extensor muscles of the head (as we have estimated their mean action line) must exert a force of 11.6 lb. to support the head in the position shown, and the reacting force between the occiput and the first cervical vertebra is 19.5 lb.

In the graphic solution of this problem (Fig. 7.8A), the magnitude and direction of W and the direction of M and B are known. We can solve for the magnitudes of M and B by constructing

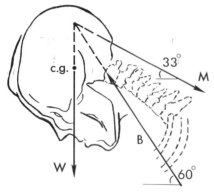

Fig. 7.7. Forces involved in maintaining a flexed position of the head: M = tension in the neck extensor muscles; W = head weight; B = force at the atlanto-occipital joint.

a vector diagram based on the known values in our problem. Starting with W, which is vertical, we next add M, which forms an angle of 33 degrees with the horizontal. The tip of B must touch the tail of vector W, and its action line forms an angle of 60 degrees with the horizontal. The juncture of vectors B and M is thus deter-

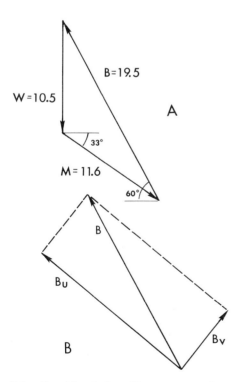

Fig. 7.8. Graphic solution of force system acting on the head. Rectangular components of force B acting at the atlanto-occipital joint are: B_u representing force at right angles to the articular supporting surface; and B_v representing the stabilizing forces at the joint which prevent the occiput from sliding forward.

mined, establishing the magnitudes of both vectors.

(We can see by inspection of Figure 7.7 that the moment arm of M approximates that of W about the atlanto-occipital joint; in this case the two forces, M and W, would be expected to be nearly equal.)

It is likely that force B in the above problem represents both reacting force at the atlanto-occipital joint and stabilization of the head on the atlas by ligaments and muscles. In the degree of flexion shown, the head would tend to slide forward off the cervical column. Muscles and ligaments at the base of the skull are in a position to counterbalance this shear force. A hypothetical analysis of components of force B is shown in Figure 7.8B. B_u represents the component contributed by compression at the atlanto-occipital joint, and B_v represents the shear-resisting effect of the suboccipital muscles and ligaments. How would the relative magnitude of these components vary as the head is flexed farther forward or extended toward the vertical position?

6. Problem

For another illustration of analysis of muscle and joint forces let us return to the deltoid muscle supporting the arm in a horizontal position. We will assume the limb weighs 7.5 lb. and the deltoid alone represents the elevator muscle force. The angle of its action line with the long axis of the humerus is 15 degrees (Fig. 7.9).

QUESTION: What is the magnitude of the tension D in the deltoid muscle and the reacting force, B, necessary for equilibrium?

SOLUTION: Force B, drawn from the point of concurrence of W and D to the glenohumeral joint, forms an angle of 6 degrees with the horizontal. Then,

$$\Sigma F_x = B \cos 6° - D \cos 15° = 0$$
$$\Sigma F_y = D \sin 15° - B \sin 6° - W = 0$$

(from $\Sigma F_x = 0$) $B = \dfrac{D \cos 15°}{\cos 6°}$

(from $\Sigma F_y = 0$)

$$D \sin 15° - \frac{D \cos 15°}{\cos 6°} \sin 6° - W = 0$$

$$D \left(\sin 15° - \frac{\cos 15°}{\cos 6°} \sin 6° \right) = W$$

$$D \left(0.259 - \frac{0.966}{0.995} 0.105 \right) = 7.5$$

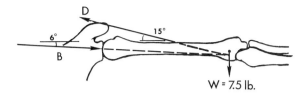

Fig. 7.9. Forces involved in supporting the arm in a horizontal position: D = pull of deltoid muscle; W = weight of limb; B = necessary third force required for equilibrium, provided by reacting force at the joint and action of the muscles inserting near the head of the humerus and exerting a downward pull.

$$D = \frac{7.5}{\left(0.259 - \frac{0.966}{0.995}\, 0.105\right)} = \frac{7.5}{0.157}$$

$$D = 47.8 \text{ lb.}$$

Solving for B,

$$B = \frac{47.8 \times 0.966}{0.995}$$

$$B = 46.4 \text{ lb.}$$

As before we find the graphic solution relatively simple, and it supports the algebraic findings.

It has been suggested that force B is the resultant of two components: active contraction of the infraspinous muscles (teres minor, infraspinatus, subscapularis) and pressure and friction at the joint.[5] It has been reported in the literature that the requirements for the downward pull of the cuff muscles, which "snub" the humeral head in the glenoid fossa, is greatest when the arm is elevated to 60 degrees and at this point the downward muscle force on the humeral head must be 9.6 times the weight of the extremity.[5]

The next two problems involve application of external forces to the body in clinical situations.

7. Problem

The forearm of a patient with weak shoulder muscles is supported in a cuff which is suspended from an overhead bar. The force in the suspension rope is 4 lb. (Fig. 7.10).

QUESTION: What is the tension in ropes A and B which form angles of 30 and 40 degrees respectively with the vertical?

SOLUTION:

$$\Sigma F_x = 0$$
$$0 = B \cos 50° - A \cos 60°$$
$$\Sigma F_y = 0$$
$$0 = 4 - B \sin 50° - A \sin 60°$$
$$B = \frac{A \cos 60°}{\cos 50°}$$
$$A \frac{\cos 60°}{\cos 50°} \sin 50° + A \sin 60° = 4$$
$$A\left(\frac{0.500}{0.643}\, 0.766 + 0.866\right) = 4$$
$$A(1.47) = 4$$
$$A = 2.7 \text{ lb.}$$
$$B = \frac{2.7 \times 0.5}{0.643}$$
$$B = 2.1 \text{ lb.}$$

Tension in rope A is 2.7 lb. and in rope B, 2.1 lb.

8. Problem

Dr. Smillie[6] has designed a device for exercising the quadriceps in which a pulley rope passes from the floor beneath the foot through a loop at the patient's heel, as shown in Figure 7.11. Tension on the other end of the rope is applied through a pulley system (not shown).

QUESTION: When a load of 20 lb. is applied to the weight pan, what must be the magnitude

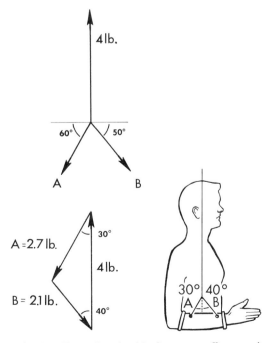

Fig. 7.10. Forces involved in forearm cuff suspension apparatus discussed in problem 8.

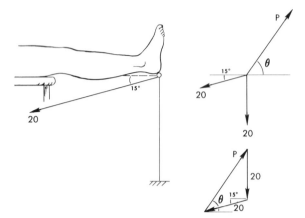

Fig. 7.11. Forces involved in Smillie device for resistance exercise for the quadriceps muscle.

and direction of the lifting force applied by the patient at the heel to balance the opposing force in the pulley ropes?

SOLUTION: In this case we know neither the value of the counterbalancing force nor its angle of application with the horizontal so we will call these P and θ respectively. We can write our equations of equilibrium as before:

$$\Sigma F_x = -20 \cos 15° + P \cos \theta = 0$$
$$\Sigma F_y = P \sin \theta - 20 \sin 15° - 20 = 0$$

From these equations we can solve for P and θ as follows:

(from $\Sigma F_x = 0$)   P cos $\theta = 20 \cos 15° = 19.32$
(from $\Sigma F_y = 0$)   P sin $\theta = 20 + 5.18 = 25.18$

We can now find tangent θ by dividing the second equation by the first, since by definition $\tan \theta = \dfrac{\sin \theta}{\cos \theta}$ (p. 78).

$$\frac{P \sin \theta}{P \cos \theta} = \frac{25.18}{19.32}$$
$$\tan \theta = 1.302$$
$$\theta = 52.5°$$

Returning to the term for P,

$$P = \frac{20 \cos 15°}{\cos 52\frac{1}{2}°} = \frac{19.32}{0.609}$$
$$P = 31.7 \text{ lb.}$$

A force of 31.7 lb. acting at an angle 52½ degrees from the horizontal is required to balance the force applied by the pulley rope. The proportion of this force which is acting at right angles to the leg (hence equivalent to the "exercise load") is P sin 52½ degrees or 31.7 × 0.793 = 25.1 lb.

Notice the similarity between this device and the leg traction apparatus discussed on page 82 in which the load applied was increased by the arrangement of the pulley ropes.

The next two sets of problems illustrate how a series of calculations may be made relative to a postural position in order to analyze forces at several joints. Let us say the man in Figure 7.12 weighs 200 lb. and he is starting to rise from a squatting position. His weight is distributed equally on both feet. Extensor muscles must act at the ankle, knee and hip to overcome the moment of gravity at each of these joints. In problems 9 through 12 we will see how forces of plantar flexion, of knee extension, and of the patella pressing against the end of the femur may be calculated with the man in the position shown and in a more erect position.

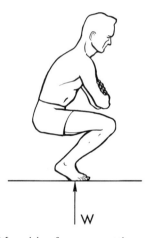

Fig. 7.12. Man rising from a squatting position. Since his weight is distributed equally on both feet and the man weighs 200 lb., W = 100 lb. on each foot.

9. Problem

The foot makes an angle of 44 degrees with the floor and the leg makes an angle of 50 degrees with the thigh.

QUESTION: What magnitude of force must be applied to the posterior aspect of the calcaneus by the tendon of Achilles, T (used here to represent the force of all the plantar flexor muscles) (Fig. 7.13)?

SOLUTION: Three forces in equilibrium must either be parallel or concurrent. Since the 100 lb. reaction force and T intersect, the action line of the force at the joint J must intersect at the same point. (The angles shown here were meas-

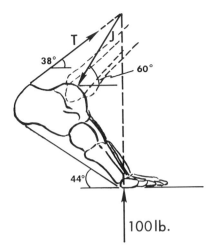

Fig. 7.13. Calculation of forces around the ankle joint (based on Fig. 7.12): T = tension in Achilles tendon; J = joint compression force.

ured from a photograph). Substituting in the equilibrium equations,

$$\Sigma F_x = 0$$
$$-J \cos 60° + T \cos 38° = 0$$
$$J = T \frac{\cos 38°}{\cos 60°}$$

$$\Sigma F_y = 0$$
$$100 + T \sin 38° - J \sin 60° = 0$$

Substituting the value of J above,

$$100 + T \sin 38° - T \frac{\cos 38°}{\cos 60°} \sin 60° = 0$$

Since $\frac{\sin}{\cos} = \tan$, we can write

$$100 + T(\sin 38° - \cos 38° \tan 60°) = 0$$
$$T = \frac{100}{\cos 38° \tan 60° - \sin 38°}$$
$$= \frac{100}{0.788 \times 1.732 - 0.6157}$$
$$T = 133.5 \text{ lb.}$$

Now the value for J can be determined:

$$J = 133.5 \frac{0.788}{0.500} = 210.4 \text{ lb.}$$

Thus the load supported at each tibio-talar joint with the body in the position shown is more than twice the body weight.

10. Problem

Now consider the position of the knee of our subject.

QUESTION: Find the force in the knee extensor muscles (acting through the patellar ligament) necessary to maintain the position shown. Vectors in Figure 7.14 have been located with the aid of a photograph and x-ray film.

SOLUTION: This time our answer will be found by a method of calculation different from that used previously. The action line of the muscle force, L, intersects the action line of the reaction on the foot as shown, and the action line of the force in the joint, J, must also pass through this point. The slopes of the vectors were determined by measurement of the distances shown in Figure 7.14.*

Substituting into the equilibrium equations, and remembering that $\sin = \dfrac{\text{side opposite}}{\text{hypotenuse}}$

and $\cos = \dfrac{\text{side adjacent}}{\text{hypotenuse}}$:

$$\Sigma F_x = 0$$
$$L \frac{15}{29.2} - J \frac{15}{35.3} = 0$$
$$J = \frac{15}{29.2} \cdot \frac{35.3}{15} L = 1.209 L$$
$$\Sigma F_y = 0$$
$$100 + \frac{25}{29.2} L - \frac{32}{35.3} J = 0$$

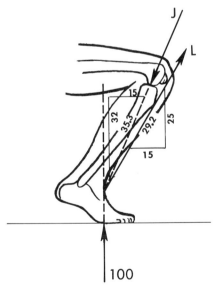

Fig. 7.14. Calculation of quadriceps tension (patellar ligament) and joint compression forces at the knee (based on Fig. 7.12 and x-ray analysis).

* Units of measurement of distances are unimportant since only a ratio of sides is needed.

Substituting for J,

$$100 + \frac{25}{29.2} L - \frac{32}{35.3} 1.209L = 0$$
$$100 + 0.856L - 0.909 \times 1.209L = 0$$
$$0.243L = 100$$
$$L = \frac{100}{0.243}$$
$$L = 411.5 \text{ lb.}$$

What is the compression force J in the knee joint in this case?

11. Problem

Let us compare force values with the knee more nearly extended, as the subject approaches the upright position.

QUESTION: Find the force in the patellar ligament when the leg is in the position shown in Figure 7.15.

SOLUTION: After the vectors were drawn, the slopes of the forces were determined by distance measurements as shown. Substituting in the equations of equilibrium,

$$\Sigma F_x = 0$$

$$L \frac{18}{29.2} - J \frac{10}{24.2} = 0$$
$$J = \frac{18}{29.2} \cdot \frac{24.2}{10} L = 1.492L$$
$$\Sigma F_y = 0$$
$$100 + \frac{23}{29.2} L - \frac{22}{24.2} J = 0$$

Substituting for J,

$$100 + 0.788L - 0.909 (1.492)L = 0$$
$$-0.788L + 1.356 L = 100$$
$$0.568 L = 100$$
$$L = 176.1 \text{ lb.}$$

As before, the value of J may now be computed.

12. Problem

Muscles and tendons frequently change direction by passing over bone and joints and in so doing they apply pressure to the underlying surface. The magnitude of the pressure can readily be determined if the force in the muscle or tendon has previously been computed.

QUESTION: Find the forces exerted by the patella on the femur in the position shown if the force in the muscle is 300 lb. (Fig. 7.16).

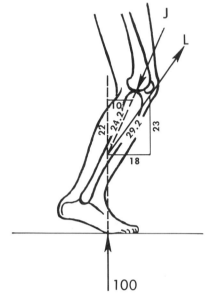

Fig. 7.15. Comparative forces in quadriceps (patellar ligament) and knee joint compression with the body approaching an upright position.

SOLUTION: The action line of the quadriceps tendon and patellar ligament were traced from an x-ray film.

$$\Sigma F_x = 0$$
$$P \cos \theta - M \cos 37° - M \cos 80° = 0$$
$$P \cos \theta = M (\cos 37° + \cos 80°)$$
$$P \cos \theta = 300 (0.799 + 0.174)$$
$$P \cos \theta = 292 \text{ lb.}$$
$$\Sigma F_y = 0$$
$$P \sin \theta + M \sin 37° - M \sin 80° = 0$$
$$P \sin \theta = M (\sin 80° - \sin 37°)$$
$$P \sin \theta = 300 (0.985 - 0.602)$$
$$P \sin \theta = 115 \text{ lb.}$$

Dividing the last equation by P cos θ = 292 lb.

$$\frac{P \sin \theta}{P \cos \theta} = \frac{115}{292}$$

and remembering that $\frac{\sin \theta}{\cos \theta} = \tan \theta$

$$\tan \theta = \frac{115}{292} = 0.393$$
$$\theta = 21.5°$$
$$P = \frac{292}{\cos \theta} = \frac{292}{0.931}$$
$$P = 314 \text{ lb.}$$

We find that the pressure of the patella against the femur is about the same as the tension in the quadriceps muscle for this particular position.

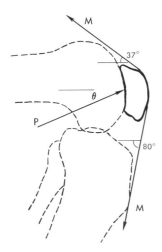

Fig. 7.16. Method of computing compression force between patella and femoral articular surface (traced from x-ray film; knee flexed 120 degrees).

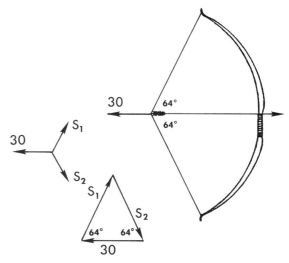

Fig. 7.17. Forces in bowstring with a pull of 30 lb. applied.

(Can you see how a vector diagram giving the resultant of forces in the patellar ligament and quadriceps tendon would also give us this information?) By the use of a series of x-ray films, femoro-patellar pressure at other angles of knee flexion can be determined.

The forces at the hip joint also can be calculated with the subject in various positions of deep knee bending, although here it is more difficult to estimate a single mean action line to represent the combined force of the hip extensor muscles than was possible in the previous set of problems.

The next three problems involve use of a bow in archery.

13. Problem

Let us consider first the force in the bowstring.

QUESTION: Find the force in the bowstring when the archer pulls back on the arrow and string with a force of 30 lb., and the included angle between the two portions of the string is 128 degrees (Fig. 7.17).

SOLUTION:

$\Sigma F_y = 0$

$\qquad S_1 \sin 64° - S_2 \sin 64° = 0$

$\qquad S_1 = S_2$

$\Sigma F_x = 0$

$\qquad S_1 \cos 64° + S_1 \cos 64° - 30 = 0$

$\qquad 2 S_1 \cos 64° = 30$

$\qquad S_1 = \dfrac{30}{2 \cos 64°} = \dfrac{30}{2 \times 0.4384}$

$\qquad S_1 = 34.2$ lb.

14. Problem

The right arm must be pulled back by the horizontal abductor muscles of the shoulder in drawing the bow (Fig. 7.18). The direction of the muscle force, M, and joint force, J, in Figure 7.19 was estimated from a photograph; the action line of the joint force, J, must pass through the point of intersection of the muscle force and the applied load. In this case, J is actually the resultant of the compression force in the glenohumeral joint and forces in surrounding joint structures stabilizing the shoulder in the necessary position.

Fig. 7.18. Archer drawing bow, as analyzed in problems 14 and 15.

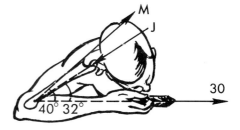

Fig. 7.19. Analysis of muscle force required at the shoulder to maintain the arm in horizontal abduction; M = posterior deltoid; J = force at the glenohumeral joint.

QUESTION: Find the force in the posterior deltoid muscle of the right shoulder.

SOLUTION: Substituting in the equilibrium equations,

$$\Sigma F_x = 0$$
$$M \cos 40° - J \cos 32° + 30 = 0$$
$$\Sigma F_y = 0$$
$$M \sin 40° - J \sin 32° = 0$$
$$J = \frac{M \sin 40°}{\sin 32°}$$

Substituting for J in the first equation,

$$M \cos 40° - \frac{M \sin 40°}{\sin 32°} \cos 32° + 30 = 0$$
$$M\left(\cos 40° - \frac{\sin 40°}{\sin 32°} \cos 32°\right) + 30 = 0$$
$$0.261 M = 30$$
$$M = 115 \text{ lb.}$$

The force, J, is 139 lb. in this case.

15. Problem

Since the bow exerts a force on the outstretched left arm in the plane of the bowstring, a component of this force will tend to push the humerus backward against the lateral border of the scapula, and another component will tend to swing the arm across the chest into horizontal adduction.

QUESTION: What force must be exerted by the posterior deltoid muscle to prevent horizontal adduction of the arm? (Fig. 7.20; measurements from a photograph.)

SOLUTION:

$$\Sigma F_x = 0$$
$$J \cos 19° - M \cos 24° - 30 = 0$$
$$\Sigma F_y = 0$$
$$M \sin 24° - J \sin 19° = 0$$
$$J = \frac{M \sin 24°}{\sin 19°}$$

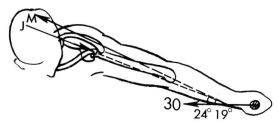

Fig. 7.20.   Analysis of muscle force required to maintain horizontal abduction of the left arm; M = posterior deltoid; J = force at the glenohumeral joint.

Substituting for J in the first equation,

$$M \frac{\sin 24°}{\sin 19°} \cos 19° - M \cos 24° - 30 = 0$$
$$M\left(\frac{\sin 24°}{\sin 19°} \cos 19° - \cos 24°\right) = 30$$
$$M\left(\frac{0.407}{0.326} 0.945 - 0.913\right) = 30$$
$$0.263 M = 30$$
$$M = 114 \text{ lb.}$$

Here the magnitude of J is 1.248M or 142 lb. If the plane of the scapula is aligned with the humerus in this position, the force which must be provided by the serratus anterior for scapular abduction is nearly five times the pull exerted on the arrow.

It may readily be seen how many additional analysis problems can be approached using the principles of the concurrent force system. In interpreting the answers obtained by this method, the assumptions necessary in formulating the problem should be kept in mind. The validity of the answers obtained is directly proportional to the accuracy and precision with which the characteristics of forces in the problems can be defined. In instances where considerable simplification is required, the findings will be less realistic than where the forces involved can be sharply defined in terms of location, magnitude, action line and direction.

General Force System

If we encounter a system of forces in a plane which does not fit into any of the previous categories—linear, parallel, or concurrent—we are dealing with a general force system. A general force system in equilibrium always includes at least four forces. A system of three forces in equilibrium must fall into one of the categories already considered. For examples of general force systems we may return to previous problems in which the weight of the part was omitted. For instance, consider again the Russell traction apparatus shown in Figure 6.12, p. 75, with a resultant force in line with the femur. Suppose we add the weight of the leg and foot (8 lb.) to the computation of the resultant force. We find that the force system does not fit into any of our previous classifications. As before, in problems involving the general force system we may be required to find the resultant of a number of forces or we may be dealing with an object known to be in equilibrium.

Resultants. In a general force system it is possible to have either a force or a couple as a resultant, as was true in the case of the parallel system. If we first break up each of the forces into a horizontal and vertical component, replacing the original forces with these components, we see that we have two parallel force systems—one acting in the horizontal direction and the other in the vertical direction. We determined previously that the resultant of the parallel force system was equal to the algebraic sum of the individual forces. In the present case the resultant of the horizontal parallel system will be equal to the sum of the horizontal components of the original forces, and the magnitude of the resultant of the vertical parallel system will be equal to the sum of the vertical components of the original forces. We now have one resultant in the horizontal direction and a second in the vertical direction. These may be combined by using Pythagoras' theorem: $R = \sqrt{\Sigma F_x{}^2 + \Sigma F_y{}^2}$. The direction of the action line of this force can be obtained as before from the equation:

$$\cos \theta = \frac{\Sigma F_x}{R} \left(\text{or} \sin \theta = \frac{\Sigma F_y}{R} \text{ or } \tan \theta = \frac{\Sigma F_y}{\Sigma F_x} \right).$$

Up to this point, finding the resultant is identical with the method used in the concurrent force system. But in the case of the concurrent system, we knew that the resultant had to pass through the point of concurrence of the original forces. In this case there is no such point, and while we know the magnitude of the resultant force and the direction of its action line, the position of the action line must still be determined. To locate its position we make use of the principle of moments which states that the moment of the resultant is equal to the sum of the moments of the individual forces of the system about any point: $Ra = \Sigma M_0$, where a is the perpendicular distance from point 0 to the action line of the resultant force, and ΣM_0 is the sum of the moments of the original forces about any point 0. In actual practice it is easier to take the moments of the rectangular components F_x and F_y about point 0 than to compute the lengths of the moment arms of the original forces.

To find the resultant of the forces shown in Figure 7.21 by the algebraic method, a tabular form of analysis will be convenient, similar to that used with the parallel force system. The magnitude of each force is entered in the left-hand column, followed by the angle the force makes with the horizontal. The next two columns contain the magnitudes of the horizontal and vertical components respectively of the original

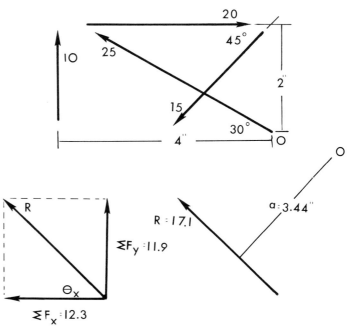

Fig. 7.21. Vector diagram of a general force system.

forces. In the two columns on the right we will enter the moment of each component force about point 0; this point may be selected arbitrarily, but it is convenient to place it on the action line of at least one of the forces to reduce the necessary computations. Clockwise moments will be negative. The sums of the moments in the two right-hand columns are added algebraically to obtain the moment of the force system about point 0:

$$\Sigma M_0 = -58.8 \text{ in. lb. (clockwise)}$$

F	θ	$F_x =$ $F \cos \theta$	$F_y =$ $F \sin \theta$	MOMENT OF F_x ABOUT 0	MOMENT OF F_y ABOUT 0
10	90	0	+10.0	0	−40
20	0	+20.0	0	−40	0
15	45	−10.6	−10.6	21.2	0
25	30	−21.7	+12.5	0	0
		$\Sigma -12.3$	$\Sigma 11.9$	$\Sigma -18.8$	$\Sigma -40$

Next, the magnitude of the resultant is determined by the familiar procedure,

$$R = \sqrt{(12.3)^2 + (11.9)^2} = 17.1 \text{ lb.}$$

The angle made by the action line of the resultant with the horizontal is found by:

$$\sin \theta_x = \frac{11.9}{17.1} = 0.696$$
$$\theta_x = 44°$$

Finally, the perpendicular distance from point 0 to the action line of the resultant force is determined:

$$a = \frac{\Sigma M_0}{R} = \frac{58.8}{17.1} = 3.44 \text{ in.}$$

Since the sum of the moments about 0 was found to be negative, or clockwise, the resultant force must be below and to the left of point 0.

In the event that both F_x and F_y equal zero, the resultant may be a couple.

$$C = \Sigma M$$

The graphic solution for the resultant of the general system is the same as that for the concurrent system to obtain the magnitude and direction of the resultant force. It is obtained by drawing a vector diagram of the forces with the tail of one vector touching the tip of the preceding one. The resultant is represented by the line from the tail of the first vector to the tip of the last. The position of the action line is obtained graphically in the same manner as was used in the parallel force system.

1. Problem

Consider a traction system for fixation of the femur with the weight of the leg and foot, 8 lb., acting at the center of gravity (Fig. 7.22). A 10 lb. load is applied to the rope.

QUESTION: Find the resultant of all the forces acting at the knee.

SOLUTION: The first step is to draw all the forces on the leg and foot in their proper location. Substituting in the equations defining the resultant,

$$R_x = \Sigma F_x$$
$$R_x = -10 \cos 61° - 10 \cos 17° - 10 \cos 19°$$
$$R_x = -10 \times 0.4848 - 10 \times 0.9563$$
$$\qquad\qquad\qquad\qquad - 10 \times 0.9455$$
$$R_x = -23.87 \text{ lb.}$$
$$R_y = \Sigma F_y$$
$$R_y = 10 \sin 61° + 10 \sin 17° - 10 \sin 19° - 8$$
$$R_y = 10 \times 0.8746 + 10 \times 0.2924$$
$$\qquad\qquad\qquad\qquad - 10 \times 0.3256 - 8$$
$$R_y = +0.414 \text{ lb.}$$
$$R = \sqrt{F_x^2 + F_y^2} = \sqrt{23.87^2 + 0.414^2}$$
$$R = 23.9 \text{ lb.}$$
$$\text{Sin } \theta_x = \frac{\Sigma F_y}{R} = \frac{0.414}{23.9}$$
$$\qquad = 0.0173$$
$$\theta_x = 1°$$

In taking moments to find the position of the action line of the resultant, it is generally easier to take moments of the horizontal and vertical components of the original forces than to find the perpendicular distances to the action lines from the selected moment center. Careful selection of the moment center can also simplify the problem appreciably. In this case taking moments about point 0, we have

$$Ra = \Sigma M_0$$
$$23.9a = -8 \times 13 + 10 \sin 61° \times 23$$

Note that all other forces or components pass through the moment center selected.

$$23.9a = 98$$
$$a = \frac{98}{23.9}$$
$$a = 4.1 \text{ in.}$$

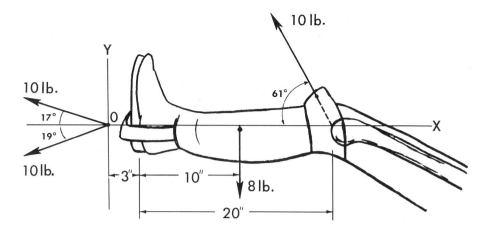

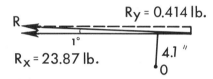

Fig. 7.22. Computation of resultant force in a traction system including weight of leg and foot.

The position of the action line must be such that the resultant produces a positive or counter clockwise moment about point 0. Since the resultant is directed to the left it will have to be placed above the moment center 0.

The resultant of the entire force system is now found to be nearly parallel to the tibia rather than to the femur. When this type of traction apparatus is applied clinically for fixation of femoral fractures, a separate rope may suspend the leg from the overhead bar to eliminate the effect of leg weight on the forces applied to the femur.

The Equilibrium Problem. Let us now turn our attention to an equilibrium problem. Suppose a 150 lb. man is exercising on a rowing machine. The seat which supports him rests on two rollers and he is pulling horizontally on the oars with a force of 50 lb. The free body diagram of the man is shown in Figure 7.23. We note that this group of forces constitutes a general system, and so we must first determine the conditions of equilibrium for this type of force system. Since the resultant must vanish for equilibrium to exist, the equations

$$\Sigma F_x = 0$$
$$\Sigma F_y = 0$$
$$\Sigma M_0 = 0$$

will define the equilibrium condition for the general force system. Note that for this type of force system three independent equations are available; therefore three unknowns can be determined.*

In general, problems that have more unknowns than the number of independent equations of equilibrium for the type of force system involved are *statically indeterminate* and cannot be solved with the equations of statics. If some relationship between several of the unknowns exists it may be possible to obtain a solution. An example might be the case of two muscles acting together where only one force can be found by the use of the pertinent equations. If the relationship between the distribution of force in each of the two muscles can be expressed mathematically, for exam-

---

* Two additional sets of equations are available for the solution of general equilibrium problems. These are

$$\Sigma F_x = 0$$
$$\Sigma M_A = 0$$
$$\Sigma M_B = 0$$

where points A and B are not on a line perpendicular to the X axis, and

$$\Sigma M_A = 0$$
$$\Sigma M_B = 0$$
$$\Sigma M_C = 0$$

where points A, B and C are not on a straight line.

ple as a function of their cross sectional area, then the force in each can be determined.

2. Problem

Consider the man exercising on the rowing machine shown in Figure 7.23.

QUESTION: Determine the force between him and the seat, and the X and Y components of the force on his feet.

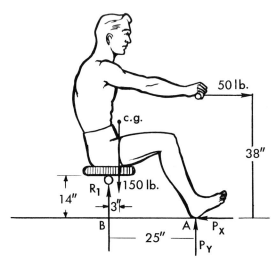

Fig. 7.23.   Patient exercising on a rowing machine. P_x and P_y represent reacting forces on the foot in the horizontal and vertical planes. R_1 = reacting force at the seat supporting the patient.

SOLUTION: Substituting into one of the sets of the equations of equilibrium for the general force system,

$$\Sigma M_A = 0 \text{ (CW moments +)}$$
$$R_1 \times 25 - 150 \times 22 + 50 \times 38 = 0$$
$$25R_1 = 1400$$
$$R_1 = 56 \text{ lb.}$$

$$\Sigma F_x = 0$$
$$50 - P_x = 0$$
$$P_x = 50 \text{ lb.}$$
$$\Sigma F_y = 0$$
$$R_1 - 150 + P_y = 0$$
$$56 - 150 + P_y = 0$$
$$P_y = 94 \text{ lb.}$$

Can you now find the single force acting upward against the heel?

The choice of direction of the coordinate axes is of importance from the standpoint of simplicity of our equations. In the majority of cases the coordinate axes are made horizontal and vertical, but if we have one group of forces acting at an angle of 30 degrees with the horizontal, for example, and another group acting at right angles to the first group, it is obvious that the equations of equilibrium will have the simplest form if we choose the X axis parallel to one set of forces and the Y axis parallel to the other set. The choice of moment centers is also of prime importance. If properly chosen, the equations of equilibrium generally become quite simple and solutions are obtained with the least amount of work.

3. Problem

A patient is using a pulley rope apparatus to strengthen his quadriceps (Fig. 7.24). His leg and foot weigh 6 lb. and a load of 20 lb. is applied to the pulley rope.

QUESTION: Find the magnitude of tension, Q, in the quadriceps necessary to maintain the position illustrated, the compression force, B, at the knee joint, and the action line of B.

SOLUTION: In setting up a free body diagram of the leg and foot, we replace the femur with force B but must guess at its action line at this point. The diagram indicates that the type of force system involved is general, in one plane, so that all three equations of equilibrium are required. Since the direction of the majority of the forces is given with respect to the axis of the leg, we will place one of the coordinate axes in this direction and the other at right angles to it. The next step is the selection of a moment center. The rule to follow whenever possible is to choose a point through which all the unknown

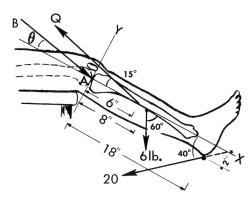

Fig. 7.24.   Quadriceps resistance exercises applied through a pulley system; free body diagram for general force system analysis.

forces pass with the exception of one. The moment equation about this point will then contain only one unknown which may be determined from this single equation. Our choice of moment center in this case is therefore point A, at the juncture of femur and tibia.

Filling in the equations of equilibrium,

$\Sigma F_x = 0$
$-20 \cos 40° + 6 \cos 60° - Q \cos 15° + B \cos \theta = 0$

$\Sigma F_y = 0$
$-20 \sin 40° - 6 \sin 60° + Q \sin 15° - B \sin \theta = 0$

$\Sigma M_A = 0$; CCW moments +
$Q \sin 15 \times 6 - 6 \sin 60 \times 8 - 20 \sin 40 \times 18 - 20 \cos 40 \times 2 = 0$

In solving for unknown values we will start with the third equation since it contains only one, Q.

$Q = \dfrac{6 \sin 60° \times 8 + 20 \sin 40° \times 18 + 20 \cos 40 \times 2}{\sin 15° \times 6}$

$Q = \dfrac{6 \times 0.866 \times 8 + 20 \times 0.643 \times 18 + 20 \times 0.766 \times 2}{0.259 \times 6}$

$Q = 196$ lb.

From $\Sigma F_x = 0$

$\Sigma F_x = -20(0.766) + 6(0.500) - 196(0.966) + B \cos \theta = 0$

$-15.3 + 3 - 189.3 = -B \cos \theta$
$B \cos \theta = 202$ lb.

from $\Sigma F_y = 0$
$\Sigma F_y = -20(0.643) - 6(0.866) + 196(0.259) - B \sin \theta = 0$

$-12.9 - 5.2 + 50.8 = B \sin \theta$
$B \sin \theta = 33$ lb.

Solving for θ, $\dfrac{B \sin \theta}{B \cos \theta} = \tan \theta$

$\tan \theta = \dfrac{33}{202} = 0.163$
$\theta = 9°$

Finally, solving for B, from $\Sigma F_x = 0$
$B \cos \theta = 202$
$B = \dfrac{202}{\cos \theta} = \dfrac{202}{0.9877}$
$B = 204$ lb.

For the last step in the solution we might have used the formula $\Sigma F_y = 0$ just as well.

According to these computations, a tension of 196 lb. in the quadriceps is needed to support the leg and foot and to oppose a pulley load of 20 lb. applied at an angle of 40 degrees to the long axis of the leg. The compression force at the knee joint is 204 lb. acting at an angle of 9 degrees with the X axis.

In the next three problems, the force applied to the femoral head under various conditions is considered. This is particularly important to know in the designing of hip prostheses. When the body weight is supported equally on both feet, half the supra-femoral weight falls on each hip joint. In walking, it is necessary for the entire supported mass to be distributed alternately on each hip joint. We will calculate hip joint compression forces in unilateral weight-bearing in the case of a 200 lb. man with no load, with a suitcase held in one hand, and with a suitcase held in each hand. (A body weight of 200 lb. has been selected for convenience. Results can be applied to persons of any weight by multiplying the results obtained here by W/200. Thus for a 140 lb. person, results could be multiplied by $^{140}/_{200}$ or 0.7.)

4. Problem

A 200 lb. man is standing on one foot.

QUESTION: Find the force on the head of the supporting femur.

SOLUTION: We will make use of a computation from a previous problem (p. 95), which determined that the direction of the resultant of the hip abductor muscle group acting at the greater trochanter made an angle of 71 degrees with the horizontal. The other dimensions required have been obtained from measurements of x-ray films (Fig. 7.25).

From a consideration of a free body diagram of the entire body we determine the reaction of the ground on the foot to be 200 lb. Adding the weight of the entire limb through its center of gravity, the X and Y components of the reaction at the hip joint and the muscle force at the greater trochanter completes the free body diagram of the limb. In this problem we have a general force system, and the equations of equilibrium are

$$F_x = 0$$
$$F_y = 0$$
$$M_o = 0$$

Substituting in these equations, and taking the moment center, O, at the point where the muscle force is applied to the greater trochanter, we have

(from $F_x = 0$) $M \cos 71° - J_x = 0$
(from $F_y = 0$)
$$200 + M \sin 71° - 31 - J_y = 0$$
(from $M_o = 0$)
$$2.75 J_y + 31 \times 4 - 200 \times 7 = 0$$
$$2.75 J_y = 1276$$
$$J_y = 464.0 \text{ lb.}$$
(from $F_y = 0$)
$$200 + M \sin 71° - 31 - 464 = 0$$
$$M = \frac{295}{\sin 71°} = \frac{295}{0.945}$$
$$M = 312 \text{ lb.}$$
(from $F_x = 0$)
$$J_x = M \cos 71° = 312 \times 0.326$$
$$J_x = 102 \text{ lb.}$$
$$J = \sqrt{J_x^2 + J_y^2} = \sqrt{102^2 + 464.0^2}$$
$$J = 475 \text{ lb.}$$
$$\tan \theta = \frac{J_y}{J_x} = \frac{475}{102} = 4.67$$
$$\theta_x = 78°$$

The femoral head supports a force of 475 lb. acting at an angle of 78 degrees from horizontal.

5. Problem

The 200 lb. man in the previous problem now carries a 100 lb. bag in his left hand while standing on his right foot. The center of gravity of the bag is 12 inches from his center of gravity (Fig. 7.26).

QUESTION: Find the force on the head of the supporting femur.

SOLUTION: The first step in the solution will be to locate the combined center of gravity of the man and bag, since his right foot will have to be directly under this point. Taking moments about the man's center of gravity,

$$100 \times 12 = 300X$$

Since the resultant force R is 300 lb.,

$$X = 4 \text{ in.}$$

Now the reaction force through the foot must be 4 inches to the left of the center line of the body and new distances to the action lines of the forces must be computed and inserted into the free body diagram. Substituting in the equations of equilibrium,

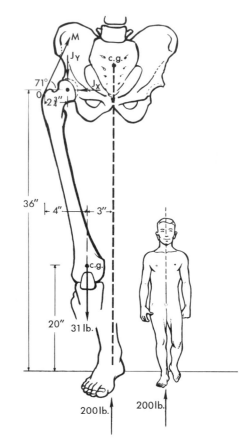

Fig. 7.25.   Determination of the compression force on the supporting femoral head in unilateral weight-bearing.

$F_x = 0$
$$M \cos 71° - J_x = 0$$
$F_y = 0$
$$300 + M \sin 71° - 31 - J_y = 0$$
$M_o = 0$
$$2.75 J_y + 31 \times 5.75 - 300 \times 11 = 0$$
$$2.75 J_y = 3122 \text{ lb.}$$
$$J_y = 1135 \text{ lb.}$$
$$300 + M \sin 71° - 31 - 1135 = 0$$
$$M = \frac{866}{\sin 71°} = \frac{866}{0.945}$$
$$M = 917 \text{ lb.}$$
$$J_x = 917 \cos 71° = 917 \times 0.326$$
$$J_x = 299 \text{ lb.}$$
$$J = \sqrt{J_x^2 + J_y^2} = \sqrt{299^2 + 1135^2}$$
$$J = 1174 \text{ lb.}$$
$$\tan \theta_x = \frac{J_y}{J_x} = \frac{1135}{299} = 3.799$$
$$\theta_x = 75°$$

In this case the femoral head supports a force of 1174 lb. with an action line forming an angle of

75 degrees with the horizontal plane. The abductor muscle group must supply a force of 917 lb. to maintain this position of the pelvis.

6. Problem

The 200 lb. man now carries a 100 lb. bag in each hand while walking very slowly.

QUESTION: What is the force on the head of the supporting femur when all of the weight is on one foot?

SOLUTION: For this problem we can use the same free body diagram as in problem 4 since the combined center of gravity of the man and the bags is located in the midline. We must change the ground reaction force to 400 lb. Substituting in the equations of equilibrium,

$$\Sigma F_x = 0 \quad M \cos 71° - J_x = 0$$
$$\Sigma F_y = 0 \quad 400 + M \sin 71° - 31 - J_y = 0$$
$$\Sigma M_o = 0 \quad 2.75 J_y + 31 \times 4 - 400 \times 7 = 0$$
$$J_y = 973 \text{ lb.}$$
$$400 + M \sin 71° - 31 - 973 = 0$$
$$M = \frac{604}{\sin 71°} = \frac{604}{0.9455}$$
$$M = 639 \text{ lb.}$$
$$J_x = 639 \cos 71° = 639 \times 0.326$$
$$J_x = 208 \text{ lb.}$$
$$J = \sqrt{J_x^2 + J_y^2} = \sqrt{208^2 + 973^2}$$
$$J = 995 \text{ lb.}$$
$$\tan \theta = \frac{J_y}{J_x} = \frac{973}{208} = 4.67$$
$$\theta = 78°$$

These findings indicate that when a load is carried on one side of the body the force in the opposite supporting hip during walking is much greater than when the load is distributed on either side. This is true even when the bilateral load is twice as great as the unilateral load. The demand on the hip abductor muscles varies in the same manner, being greatest when a load is carried on the contralateral side. Carrying loads in the midline of the body, as in a knapsack or on the head or shoulders, is effective in reducing required musculoskeletal force.

For another example of a general force system let us return to problem 9, p. 100, in which a 200 lb. man is rising from a deep knee bend position. In computation of the forces at the ankle, the problem was treated previously as a concurrent system of forces. If we now include the weight of the foot in the solution, we have a gen-

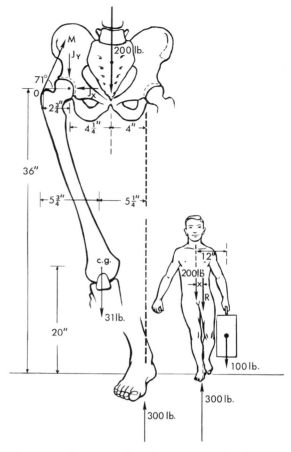

Fig. 7.26. Determination of the compression force on the supporting femoral head in unilateral weight-bearing with a weight held in the opposite hand.

eral force system. In order to set up the free body diagram, measurements as shown in Figure 7.27 were made from an x-ray film. The weight of the foot is 3 lb.

7. Problem

Consider the 200 lb. man in problem 9, p. 100.

QUESTION: Find the force, T, in the Achilles tendon needed to maintain the position of the ankle joint taking the weight of the foot into account. Find also the compression force on the talus and locate its action line.

SOLUTION:

$$\Sigma F_x = 0$$
$$T \cos 38° = J_x$$
$$\Sigma F_y = 0$$
$$100 + T \sin 38 - 3 - J_y = 0$$

Taking the attachment of the Achilles tendon as moment center,

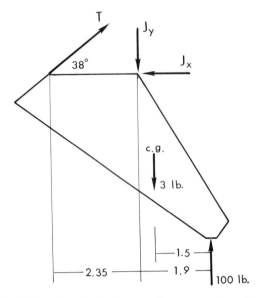

Fig. 7.27. Free body diagram for computation of tendon of Achilles tension and tibio-talar compression force in deep knee-bend position.

$$\Sigma M_o = 0$$
$$2.35\, J_y + 3 \times 2.75 - 100 \times 4.25 = 0$$
$$2.35 J_y = 417$$
$$J_y = 177.5 \text{ lb.}$$
$$100 + T \sin 38 - 3 - 177.5 = 0$$
$$0.6157\, T = 80.5$$
$$T = 130.7 \text{ lb.}$$
$$J_x = 130.7 \cos 38° = 130.7 \times 0.788$$
$$J_x = 103 \text{ lb.}$$
$$J = \sqrt{103^2 + 177.5^2}$$
$$J = 205.2 \text{ lb.}$$
$$\tan \theta_x = \frac{177.5}{103} = 1.723$$
$$\theta_x = 60°$$

These forces differ very little from those obtained in problem 9 where the weight of the foot was neglected, since its magnitude is very small in comparison with the other forces acting in the problem.

8. Problem

As a final example consider forces at the knee of the 200 lb. man in Figure 7.12. Figure 7.28 shows the free body diagram of the leg and foot; measurements were taken from a photograph and x-ray film.* The knee is flexed more sharply here than in previous problems (nos. 10 and 11, p. 101). J_x and J_y represent forces at the knee

joint in the horizontal and vertical planes respectively.

QUESTION: Find the force in the quadriceps (patellar ligament) and the magnitude and action line of the compression force at the knee joint.

SOLUTION: As before, we will define the slope of the quadriceps force L by setting up a right triangle along its action line; remember that $\cos \theta = \dfrac{\text{side adjacent}}{\text{hypotenuse}}$ and $\sin \theta = \dfrac{\text{side opposite}}{\text{hypotenuse}}$:

$$\Sigma F_x = 0$$
$$\frac{2.7}{3.36} L - J_x = 0$$
$$\Sigma F_y = 0$$
$$100 - 12 - J_y + \frac{2}{3.36} L = 0$$

Moments are taken about the juncture of the action lines of the J_y component of the joint compression force and the quadriceps force.

$$\Sigma M_0 = 0$$
$$1.5\, J_x + 7 \times 12 - 14 \times 100 = 0$$
$$J_x = \frac{1316}{1.5} = 877 \text{ lb.}$$
$$L = \frac{3.36}{2.7} J_x = \frac{3.36}{2.7} 877$$
$$L = 1092 \text{ lb.}$$
$$100 - 12 - J_y + \frac{2}{3.36} 1092 = 0$$
$$J_y = 738 \text{ lb.}$$
$$J = \sqrt{J_x^2 + J_y^2} = \sqrt{877^2 + 738^2}$$
$$J = 1145 \text{ lb.}$$
$$\tan \theta_x = \frac{738}{877} = 0.842$$
$$\theta_x = 40°$$

From the results in this problem and in problems 10 and 11, p. 101, it is apparent that the tension force in the quadriceps and compression force in the knee joint increase rapidly with deep knee bending. In the relaxed standing position no activity is necessary in the quadriceps muscle since the action line of the supported

* In the series of x-ray films used for these problems, the action line of quadriceps force (acting through the patellar ligament) was found to intersect the long axis of the leg during the first 60 degrees of knee flexion, to lie parallel to the anterior crest of the tibia at about 60 to 65 degrees of flexion, and to diverge increasingly from the leg axis as the knee approached full flexion.

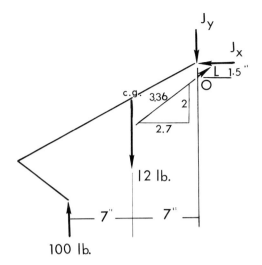

Fig. 7.28. Free body diagram for computation of quadriceps (patellar ligament) tension and compression force between femur and tibia in deep knee bend position.

body weight falls anterior to the axis of rotation at the knee. In this position the force compressing the femoral and tibial surfaces is due to the supra-tibial body weight and also to tension in the posterior knee structures which stabilize the joint (prevent hyperextension). As the knees flex in deep knee bending, the moment of gravity rapidly increases. In the three positions of knee bending analyzed in this text, the joint force was found to vary from 263 lb. to 1145 lb., and the quadriceps tension ranged from 176 lb. to 1092 lb.

Results of these calculations can be compared with those obtained when loads are applied in various types of knee resistance exercises such as pulley systems, deLorme boot, NK table, Storms board, or Smillie pulley device. Apparatus used clinically that applies maximum resistance when the knee is extended, as in lifting a free weight in the sitting position, provides resistance in a pattern contrary to normal functional use. That is, gravitational moments about the knee in daily activity are greatest when the joint is flexed as in stair climbing, rising from a chair, and stooping.

We have seen in this chapter how forces involved in many body postures can be calculated, as well as the effects of external forces and force systems applied to the body. A given problem may become more complex as more factors are considered, as in adding the weight of the part

which may be a minor consideration in some instances. The choice of procedure will depend on how precise an answer is desired. In the next chapter another factor not yet considered will be discussed—the factor of friction.

Questions

1. If a head traction apparatus has two vertical strands and a third strand making an angle of 50 degrees with the horizontal plane, what force is applied to the head sling when a load of 5 lb. is placed on the end of the rope?

2. How might you set up a traction apparatus for stretching the cervical spine so that a force equal to 1.5 times head weight could be applied to a 150 lb. patient? Mention at least three possible arrangements.

3. In problem 5, p. 97, find algebraically the magnitudes of component forces B_u and B_v. What specific anatomical structures could supply these forces? Calculate changes in the magnitude of these components at different points in the range of motion of the head.

4. Set up a free body diagram and find the solution to problem 6, p. 98, if a 10 lb. weight is held in the hand. Estimate distances needed in your answer. (This now becomes a general force system problem.)

5. If you have not already done so, calculate the compression force, J, on the joint in problems 10 and 11, p. 101.

6. Returning to problem 13, p. 103, what force does the bowstring exert on the arrow at the instant of release if the included angle between the two portions of the string is 100 degrees and the force on the string is 60 lb.?

7. (a) Using the measurements in problem 3, p. 108, calculate quadriceps tension and joint compression force at the knee if a 30 lb. deLorme boot and weights replace the pulley rope. Estimate distances needed.

   (b) Repeat the solution with the subject's knee in full extension.

   (c) Compare your answers in (a) and (b) with the force requirements of deep knee bending in the case of a 150 lb. man.

8. Review some of the problems in this chapter in which "mean" action lines of muscle forces have been estimated. Apply slightly different action lines in order to observe the mag-

nitude of "error" introduced by such estimates.

9. Set up and solve some concurrent and general force system problems of your own. If possible, think of an equilibrium problem which may be analyzed first as a concurrent force system and then, by adding the weight of the part, as a general force system. Compare answers obtained by each method.

Bibliography

1. McCusker, H.: Cervical traction sling. *Phys. Therapy Rev., 36*:763–4, 1956.

2. Inman, V. T.: Functional aspects of the abductor muscles of the hip. *J. Bone Joint Surg. (Amer.), 29*:607–619, 1947.

3. Joseph, J., and Nightingale, A.: Electromyography of muscles of posture: leg muscles in males. *J. Physiol., 117*:484–491, 1952.

4. Smith, J. W.: The forces operating at the human ankle joint during standing. *J. Anat., 91*:545–564, 1957.

5. Inman, V. T., Saunders, J. B. M., and Abbott, L. C.: Observations on the function of the shoulder joint. *J. Bone Joint Surg. (Amer.), 26*:1–30, 1944.

6. Allis, J. B.: Smillie board—a quadriceps exerciser. *Phys. Therapy Rev., 35*:374–377, 1955.

CHAPTER EIGHT

Friction

Friction is generally necessary for movement to start. Walking requires adequate friction between the sole of the foot and the floor, so that the foot will not slip forward or backward and the effect of limb extension can be imparted to the trunk. Lack of friction on icy surfaces is compensated for by hobnails on boots or chains on tires. Friction is necessary to the operation of a self-propelled vehicle, not only to start it and keep it going but to stop it as well. A wheelchair can be pushed only because of the friction developed between the pusher's shoes and the floor, and friction must likewise be developed between the wheels and the floor so they will turn and not slide. Crutches and canes are stable due to friction between their tips and the floor; this is often increased by a rubber tip which has a high coefficient of friction with the floor.

Many friction devices are used in exercise equipment to grade resistance to movement, as with a shoulder wheel or stationary bicycle. Brakes on wheelchairs and locks on bed casters utilize the principles of friction. Application of cervical or lumbar traction to a bed patient depends on adequate opposing frictional forces developed between the patient's body and the bed.

In the operation of machines, sliding friction wastes energy. This energy is transformed into heat which may have a harmful effect on the machine, as with burned-out bearings. To reduce friction, materials having a very smooth or polished surface are used for contacting parts, or a lubricant, such as oil or grease, is placed between the moving parts. Frictional effects are then absorbed between the layers of the lubricant rather than by the surfaces in contact. Friction also exists within the human body. Normally ample lubrication is present as tendons slide within synovial sheaths at sites of wear, and the articulating surfaces of joints are bathed in synovial fluid.

When two surfaces are pressed together, as shown in Figure 8.1, a force in the lateral direction is required to make one surface slide over the other. The resistance to this force developed at the surface of contact is termed the *frictional force*. The magnitude of the force required to produce motion of one surface with respect to the other depends on: (1) how tightly the two surfaces are pressed together, and (2) the kinds of materials in contact with each other and the roughness of the surfaces. A factor called the coefficient of friction, designated by the symbol μ (mu), is used to describe the effect of different materials and the roughness of the contact surfaces. Different types of materials have different coefficients of friction; these can be determined approximately by a simple experiment since

$$F_{max} = \mu N$$

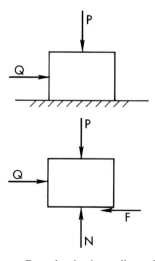

Fig. 8.1. Force, Q, pushes horizontally against a box of weight, P. The weight of the box is opposed by the normal force, N, perpendicular to the surface. The force of friction, F, opposes horizontal force, Q. Note that force, N, cannot actually be in line with P, since the couple produced by Q and F must be balanced by a couple consisting of P and N.

Where F_{max} is the maximum possible friction force, μ is the coefficient of friction, and N is the "normal" force, or force perpendicular to the surfaces in contact, pressing the surfaces together. If the force necessary to start an object sliding along a horizontal surface can be carefully measured, it will approximate (be slightly more than) the maximum force of friction between the contacting surfaces.

1. Problem

A force of 20 lb. is needed to start a 100 lb. box sliding across a wooden table.

QUESTION: What is the coefficient of friction between the box and the table?

SOLUTION: Filling in the known values in our equation, we have

$$20 = \mu\,100$$
$$\mu = \frac{20}{100}$$
$$\mu = 0.2$$

Notice that the area of contact is not important. A given force pressing the contacting surfaces together will produce a given frictional effect regardless of whether the contacting surface is large or small.

Another important point is that it takes more force to set an object in motion than to keep it moving. As long as the surfaces in contact with each other are at rest, the value of μ is constant. When motion takes place between the surfaces, μ always has a lower value than when the surfaces are at rest. It takes more force to start a sled moving than to keep it moving.

If frictional forces are equal to the applied forces which tend to make an object slide, it will remain at rest. As we have seen, the use of the coefficient of friction permits us to express mathematically the maximum frictional force which can be developed in terms of the pressure existing between surfaces in contact. All the equations of equilibrium which have previously been developed apply in problems where frictional forces are involved. An important factor which has not appeared previously is that frictional force may have any magnitude from zero to the F_{max} value. The direction of frictional force is dependent on the direction in which the object tends to move; the frictional force always acts to oppose motion, or potential motion, as shown in Figure 8.1.

Suppose a gymnasium mat rests on the floor with a child sitting on the mat (Fig. 8.2). The child and mat together weigh 30 pounds. If the coefficient of friction between the mat and floor is 0.15, the maximum frictional force which can be developed will be:

$$F_{max} = \mu N$$
$$= 0.15 \times 30$$
$$= 4.5 \text{ lb.}$$

If we push on the mat with a force of 3 lb. to the right, our equations of equilibrium show that the frictional force developed will be 3 lb. acting to the left. If we push on the mat toward the left with a force of ½ lb. the opposing frictional force developed will be ½ lb. to the right, and so on. The magnitude of the frictional force is always obtained by the equations of equilibrium, but its maximum value can never exceed F_{max}. If a 10 lb. force were to be applied to the mat, only a 4.5 lb. frictional force could be developed. In this case the mat would no longer be in equilibrium but would slide in the direction of the applied force.

Many instances of application of friction can be seen in physical therapy. As friction plates on exercise apparatus wear smooth they have to be pushed together more tightly and eventually replaced. (N must increase as μ decreases to maintain F_{max}.) Setscrews on knobs and handles work loose and must be tightened, as do bolts and nuts. In raising and lowering infrared and ultraviolet lamps, one must be certain that the friction applied by the knob and screw is adequate to maintain the weight of the lamp head in the desired position. Very heavy lamps are usually counterbalanced to reduce the friction required to support the equipment safely at various heights. Grasping a knob with the hand to turn it makes use of the friction developed between the fingers and the knob. Grasping more tightly, if the knob fails to turn, increases F_{max}. When skin traction is applied, a glue such as Mastisol may be spread on the skin to make the overlying strips of muslin or flannel adhere. Foam rubber also grips the skin firmly when applied beneath an elastic bandage,[1] the bandage providing the necessary normal force.

While there are many instances in which friction is applied clinically to good purpose, at other times we try to minimize its effects. A lubricant is used in massage so that the hands will slide smoothly over the patient's skin. An exercise board with powder sprinkled on the surface makes bed exercises easier. Surface friction is eliminated entirely in exercises in a pool or with sling suspension. In functional and assistive apparatus, swivel joints and ball bearing and roller bearing joints minimize frictional

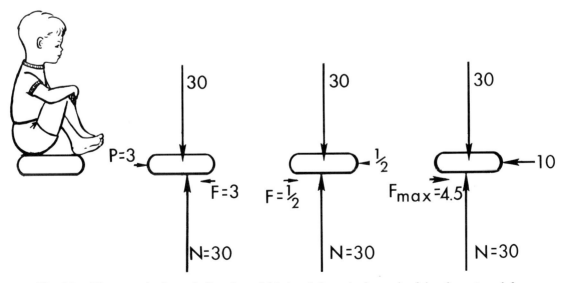

Fig. 8.2. The magnitude and direction of frictional force is determined by the external force applied, but it can never exceed F_{max}, which in this case is 4.5 lb. The figure on the right will slide, as F_{max} has been exceeded.

drag, so that the patient can utilize his strength to best advantage in movement. In braces and prostheses the requirements for free motion at joints must be balanced against requirements for stability and ruggedness of the apparatus. One of the most common means of reducing friction, of course, is by lubricating the joints. This also helps to eliminate squeaks in noisy joints.

In the solution of problems involving friction, care must be taken to obtain the correct value of the normal force or pressure between the contact surfaces. This is not always equal to the weight of the part, as will be shown in the next two problems.

2. Problem

Consider a patient with neck traction applied by calipers or tongs attached to the skull. (Fig. 8.3). Let us say the head weighs 10 lb. and the coefficient of friction between the back of the head and the bed is 0.17. The action line of the pulley force is parallel with the bed surface.

QUESTION: Find the maximum frictional force which must be overcome before the traction pull will be effective in stretching the cervical structures.

SOLUTION: The force of pulley rope, P, weight of the head, W, and the normal reacting force, N, are shown in Figure 8.3A. We know that maximum frictional force is acting in this case since motion of the head is impending, and that F_{max} must act in a direction to oppose impending motion. The equations of equilibrium can be applied, since we know that the head is at rest and not moving.

Substituting into the equation $F_{max} = \mu N$, and solving for N, we obtain:

$$F_{max} = 0.17 \times 10$$
$$= 1.7 \text{ lb.}$$

A force of 1.7 lb. on rope, P, is necessary to overcome the friction between the head and bed in this case.

3. Problem

Now consider a similar traction system in which the pulley rope forms an angle of 10 degrees with the horizontal plane, a technique sometimes used to stretch the posterior neck

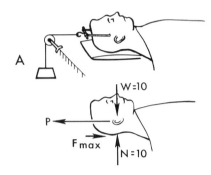

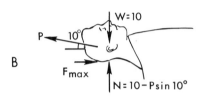

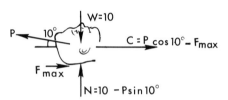

Fig. 8.3. A. Application of cervical traction through skull calipers. Head weight, W, is opposed by N, the force normal to the supporting surface; traction load P is opposed by F_{max}.

B. When the traction rope is slanted upward 10 degrees, the value of N depends on P as well as W. C represents tension on cervical structures.

structures (Fig. 8.3B). The pulley rope applies a force P.

QUESTION: Find the force P required to start the head moving upward toward the end of the bed.

SOLUTION: The same conditions apply as in the previous problem. Substituting into the equation $\Sigma F_y = 0$, and solving for N we obtain:

$$-10 + P \sin 10° + N = 0$$
$$N = 10 - P \sin 10°$$

From this equation we see that in this case N is not equal to the weight of the head but is also dependent on the force P and the angle at which it is applied. When the pulley rope is slanted upward, the maximum frictional force between the head and bed is decreased.

Suppose P, the traction load, is 12 lb. Then:

$$\Sigma F_y = 0$$
$$-10 + (12 \sin 10°) + N = 0$$
$$N = 10 - 12\,(0.174)$$
$$= 7.9 \text{ lb.}$$

Now we can determine F_{max} and the stretching force, C, applied to the cervical structures in this case.

$$F_{max} = \mu\,N$$
$$= 0.17 \times 7.9$$
$$= 1.3 \text{ lb.}$$

Of the total traction load applied, a horizontal component of 1.3 lb. will be used up in overcoming the maximum force of friction developed between the head and the bed. To determine the cervical tension, C, we will substitute in the formula $\Sigma F_x = 0$:

$$P \cos 10° - F_{max} - C = 0$$
$$12(0.985) - 1.3 = C$$
$$C = 10.5 \text{ lb.}$$

A traction load of 12 lb. under these circumstances applies a tension force of 10½ lb. to the cervical structures. It is evident that the magnitude of the normal force will decrease with larger angles of force application (increased upward slant of the traction line) and with larger upward traction loads.

In solving problems, if a proper free body diagram is drawn, showing all the forces acting, and these forces are inserted into the equations of equilibrium, the correct value of the normal force, N, can be obtained. Also, the frictional force, F, must be shown acting in the proper direction, if the direction can be ascertained from the setup of the problem. It is also important to recognize when the maximum friction force F_{max} is developed; this will be the case whenever motion is about to take place.

The Starr head traction and trolley device, described by Knocke and Knocke,[2] was designed to eliminate the friction of the occipital area against the bed and the danger of decubitus ulcer as a result (Fig. 8.4). Here the entire head is supported by a frame on wheels rolling on a track. The resistance between the head platform and track is much lower than the friction between the head and platform. Thus the head and platform move as a single unit. In-

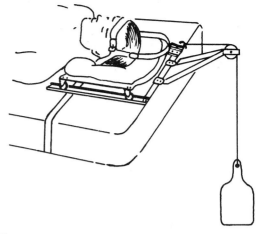

Fig. 8.4. Starr head traction device which eliminates frictional force between the occipital region and the bed. (Redrawn from Knocke and Knocke.[2])

stead of the chinpiece found in the Sayre type of halter, this device has a frontal band, making eating easier and avoiding uncomfortable pressure on the mandible. A device such as this might be used for intermittent traction or as an interim measure; continuous traction is usually applied through calipers applied to the skull.[2]

An interesting clinical use of friction in a cervical traction pulley system has been suggested by Jackson.[3] With the patient in the upright position, she has demonstrated by radiographs of the cervical spine that "the conventional amount of weight of 5 to 10 pounds (traction force) does nothing more than lift the weight of the head from the neck." However, 20 to 25 pounds resulted in distraction between the cervical vertebrae, and this was more marked with 35 pounds. For home treatment she advocates an overhead pulley system, such as that shown in Figure 8.5. When a 20 pound load is suspended from the end of the rope, according to Jackson, traction on the head halter is about 15 pounds. The discrepancy is said to be due to friction developed between the rope and the pulleys. Then "if the patient slumps or slides down in the chair, the actual pull may be increased to 25 or 30 pounds without altering the position of the weights." This would indicate that the maximum force of friction in the pulley system was reversed in direction because the head was now pulling on the system of weights. As additional force is added by the shift in posture to oppose the traction weights,

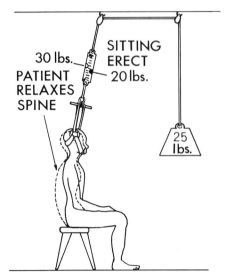

Fig. 8.5. Pulley system for applying cervical traction with the patient in the upright position. (Redrawn from Jackson.[3])

F_{max} is approached until eventually the weights would move upward. This shift in posture without movement of the weights provides a simple way for the patient himself to control the magnitude of neck traction and to grade it over a small range.

In tests of apparatus, a scale for monitoring traction forces applied through a pulley system is always placed between the patient and the first pulley to rule out the effects of friction in the system.

Commercially available power-spring traction reels attached to the bed eliminate the use of pulleys and traction weights. In these devices a revolving drum adjusts the tension in the rope to movements of the patient and maintains a constant pre-set force in the line attached to the part. Traction forces are applied by such devices assuming that adequate counterforce is available to stabilize the patient so that he will not be moved along in the direction of the traction line. In other words, the friction developed between the patient's body and the bed must never be exceeded by the traction force applied. If the patient tends to slide in the direction of the traction force, the bed may be tilted up to oppose this movement. This adds a component of the body weight to the maximum available force of friction stabilizing the patient.

Judovich[4] has investigated the friction forces associated with pelvic traction and concluded

that the usual application of 10 to 15 pounds on each side is completely neutralized by "surface traction resistance" or friction of the lower limbs. He experimented with a cadaver and three living subjects, applying weights until surface friction was exceeded. By sectioning the cadaver between lumbar vertebrae 3 and 4 and disarticulating the hips and knees, he determined that the average force necessary to overcome frictional resistance was 54 per cent of the weight of the parts or of the entire body. Judovich estimated the portion of the body distal to the lumbar 3–4 interspace to be 49 per cent of total body weight; 54 per cent of this amount is about 26 per cent of body weight, a figure which he suggests can be used to estimate frictional resistance to pelvic traction due to the weight of the lower limbs. Intermittent pelvic traction in the range of 60 to 80 pounds was recommended, "of which 40 to 50 pounds are lost in dissipating surface resistance." In the cervical region the dissipating force due to head-bed friction was said to be 6 pounds.

On the basis of these figures the coefficient of friction developed between a 150 pound patient and the bed can be determined. If the lower segments weigh 73.5 lb. (49 per cent $\times$ 150 lb.) and 54 per cent of this value (or 39.7 lb.) is the maximum force of friction, then

$$F_{max} = \mu N$$
$$39.7 = \mu\, 73.5$$
$$\mu = 0.54$$

In the case of cervical traction, if the dissipating force due to friction is 6 pounds and $\mu = 0.54$, we can compute the weight of the head as follows:

$$F_{max} = \mu N$$
$$6 = 0.54\, N$$
$$N = \frac{6}{0.54}$$
$$= 11.1\ \text{lb.}$$

This coefficient of friction is high in relation to those for other materials. The firmness of the mattress and the materials in contact with the body would be important factors affecting this value.

Judovich devised a bed with upper and lower sections, each with a separate mattress. The patient lay with his lumbar region over the division. The lower section of the bed was placed on rollers and a motor-driven mechanism moved it rhythmically back and forth in relation to the upper segment. Here the surface friction between the patient and the bed served to stabilize the upper and lower segments on the divided sections, so that the lumbar region could be stretched. If traction forces greater than maximum friction values were desired, a pelvic belt and shoulder harness could be applied.[4]

As another example, consider a friction problem involving an infrared lamp (Fig. 8.6).

4. Problem

The coefficient of friction between the floor and the lamp base is 0.22. A therapist attempts to move the lamp by pushing against the upright with force, P. The distance between the floor and the center of gravity of the lamp is 30 in. and between the floor and the therapist's hand is 38 in. The distance from a vertical line through the center of gravity of the lamp to the edge of the base is 6 in.

QUESTION: As the therapist pushes, will the lamp slide as intended or tip over?

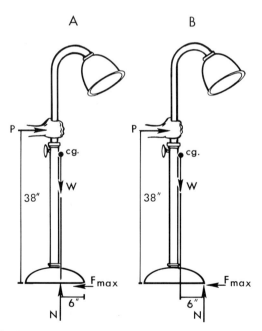

A   B

Fig. 8.6. A. Method of moving an infrared lamp, where N = normal force, P = push by therapist attempting to slide the lamp, and $\mu = 0.22$. It is assumed here that the lamp will slide.

    B. Here it is assumed that the lamp will tip over as a result of force P, so N acts at the edge of the base on the side opposite the push.

SOLUTION: We must solve the problem twice. First, we will assume the lamp will slide and solve for F_{max} and P to satisfy this condition (Fig. 8.6A). From $\Sigma F_y = 0$, we have W = N.

From our assumption of sliding,

$$F_{max} = \mu N$$
$$= 0.22 \, N$$
$$= 0.22 \, W$$
$$\Sigma F_x = 0, \, P = F_{max}$$
$$= 0.22 \, W$$

For our next solution we will assume that the lamp is about to tip over (Fig. 8.6B). The force, N, in this case will have to act at the edge of the lamp base. Taking moments about this point we have

$$P \times 38 = W \times 6$$
$$P = \frac{6 \, W}{38}$$
$$= 0.16 \, W$$

Looking at both solutions, we see that a force of 0.16W is required to tip the lamp over, while a force of 0.22W is necessary to make it slide. Therefore, if the original plan is carried through the lamp will tip.

What should the therapist do to prevent this mishap? Repeat the above computation with push, P, exerted 24 inches from the floor instead of 38 inches. Where along the upright of the lamp will the effect of P change from a tip to a slide? What effect has the size of the lamp base on this problem? Would a larger lamp base (with the same lamp weight) increase the coefficient of friction between the base and the floor? What difference would it make if the lamp head were directed toward instead of away from the pusher as shown in Figure 8.6? What difference would it make if the coefficient of friction were 0.12 between the lamp and the floor instead of 0.22?

Notice in the case of the infrared lamp that a high center of gravity will cause the lamp to tip more easily than if it is lower. The moment arm for the high center of gravity becomes very small as the lamp begins to tip (center of gravity moves rapidly toward edge of base). When the center of gravity is lower, its moment arm decreases very little with tipping, which tends to keep the lamp upright. For this reason some physical therapists make it a habit to lower all lamp heads before moving equipment around the department.

We are able to walk or run only because of the frictional force at the ground acting on the foot in the direction in which we want to move (Fig. 8.7). The importance of frictional force developed between the shoe and the ground during walking, especially at heel strike and toe-off, was mentioned earlier. Force plate studies indicate that the horizontal component of foot force at heel strike is about 15 per cent of body weight, and at toe-off, 20 per cent of body weight.[5] F_{max} must exceed these values if the foot is not to slip. The value of the normal force at these points in the gait cycle is more than body weight, due to the momentum of the body at heel strike and the thrust of plantar flexion before the toe-off. This increase in normal force helps to provide adequate stabilization for the foot. The friction developed in walking is generally less than the F_{max} value, but it may reach the F_{max} value on slippery surfaces where the coefficient of friction is reduced.

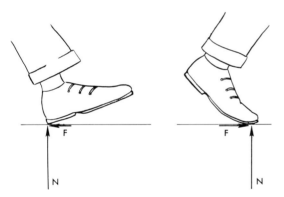

Fig. 8.7. Horizontal (shear) force at heel strike and toe off in walking. The vertical force of ground reaction, N, is more than body weight at these points in the gait cycle.

Heel strike is a more hazardous point than toe-off for a foot to slip. Fundamental gait studies have shown also that there are lateral shear forces and torques exerted against the ground by the supporting foot which must be opposed by friction.[5]

Graphic solution of friction problems. In some friction problems a graphic solution will be the easiest to use. In this procedure, F_{max} and N are combined into a single resultant force, R (Fig. 8.8). Now from the equation $F_{max} = \mu N$ we can write $\mu = F_{max}/N$.

From the relationship of the forces N and F_{max} in Figure 8.8, we see that the tan ϕ =

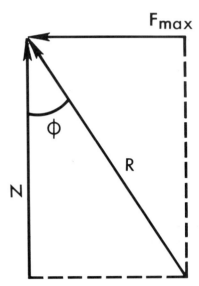

Fig. 8.8. Graphic solution of friction problem in which F_{max} and N are shown as a single resultant force, R.

F_{max}/N also, where ϕ is the angle between the normal force and the resultant, R, of the normal and maximum frictional force. Therefore $\mu = \tan \phi$, where ϕ is called the *angle of friction.* Whenever the maximum frictional force is developed, the tangent of the angle between the resultant force and the normal is equal to the coefficient of friction. For example, in Figure 8.9 suppose we are to find the minimum force, P, and the angle alpha (α) at which it must act in order to start the block of weight, W, moving if the coefficient of friction is μ. In a free body diagram we can show R, the resultant of N and F_{max}, acting at the angle of friction ϕ with the vertical. If we draw a force polygon starting with W, whose magnitude and direction are known, and R, whose direction is known, we can complete the triangle by drawing the shortest line possible from the beginning of W to the action line of R. This line will have to be at right angles to the action line of R and so will define the magnitude of P and R and the direction of P. This latter direction obviously makes an angle ϕ with the horizontal. We now have the necessary characteristics of P needed for our answer.

Tendon Friction. Friction also acts between flexible and rigid members. Thus frictional forces may exist between a tendon and a bony prominence that it passes over or between a rope and a pole that it encircles. It is a matter of everyday experience that by taking a turn of

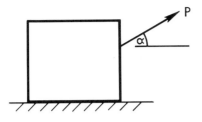

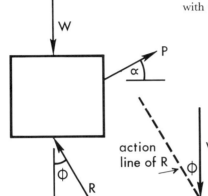

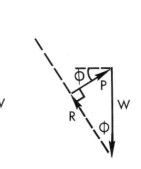

Fig. 8.9. Determination by a force polygon of the minimum force, P, necessary to move block W; P acts at angle alpha with the horizontal.

rope around a pole or capstan, it becomes much easier to resist a force pulling on the other end. If the greater force in the rope is designated as T_{max} and the lesser force as T_{min}, the relationship between them is given by the equation

$$T_{max} = T_{min} \cdot e^{\mu\alpha}$$

where e is 2.718 (the base of the natural system of logarithms), μ is the coefficient of friction between the surfaces of contact, and α is the angle of contact between the surfaces. This angle of contact must be expressed in radians. (There are 2π radians and 360 degrees in a circle, so one radian equals 57.3 degrees.) Figure 8.10 illustrates the forces acting on a rope passing over a pole. The free body diagram of the rope shows that a whole series of normal and frictional forces exist along the contact area between the rope and the pole.

Since it will be necessary to employ logarithms to obtain a solution to tendon friction problems, a brief review of the basic principles will be given. Consider the expression

$$B^L = N$$

L is called the logarithm of N to the base B, and an equivalent expression can be written thus:

$$L = Log_B N$$

By definition the logarithm of a number is the exponent to which the base must be raised in order to obtain the desired number. The common system of logarithms always uses 10 as the base and the natural system uses the base 2.718. For the common system, the following equivalent expressions can be written:

$10^1 = 10$	or	$Log_{10} 10 = 1$
$10^2 = 100$		$Log_{10} 100 = 2$
$10^3 = 1000$		$Log_{10} 1000 = 3$
$10^0 = 1$		$Log_{10} 1 = 0$
$10^{-1} = \dfrac{1}{10^1} = 0.1$		$Log_{10} 0.1 = -1$
$10^{-2} = \dfrac{1}{10^2} = 0.01$		$Log_{10} 0.01 = -2$
$10^{-3} = \dfrac{1}{10^3} = 0.001$		$Log_{10} 0.001 = -3$

The logarithms of the above numbers are very easily obtained, but suppose the logarithm of a number between 10 and 100, say 20, is desired. It is obvious that it will be somewhere between 1 and 2, and the fractional part of the value required can be obtained from a table of logarithms. The integral part of the logarithm, called the characteristic, is always obtained by inspection and is one less than the number of digits to the left of the decimal point, or a negative one more than the number of zeroes to the right of the decimal point. This may be seen by inspection of the preceding table. The fractional part is independent of the position of the decimal point, and in our example this value is 0.3010. The fractional part would be the same if the original number were 2, 20, 200, etc. The complete logarithm is the sum of the characteristic and the fractional part (called the mantissa) and for our example is 1.3010. (The logarithm of 200 would be 2.3010.)

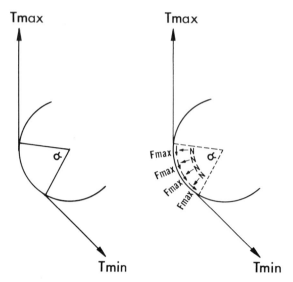

Fig. 8.10. Effect of friction on the forces in a rope or tendon passing over a surface which changes its direction.

Since the following laws exist,

$$10^n \cdot 10^m = 10^{n+m}$$
$$\frac{10^n}{10^m} = 10^{n-m}$$
$$(10^n)^m = 10^{n \cdot m}$$

we see that the product of two numbers can be obtained by adding their logarithms, the quotient of two numbers can be obtained by subtracting their logarithms, and a number can be raised to a power by multiplying its logarithm by the power.

Using these definitions and the following relationships between the natural and common system of logarithms:

$$\text{Log}_{10} 2.718 = 0.4343$$
$$\text{and Log}_e 10 = 2.3026$$

we can write the basic tendon friction equation:

$$e^{\mu\alpha} = \frac{T_{max}}{T_{min}}$$

$$\text{Log}_e \frac{T_{max}}{T_{min}} = \mu\alpha$$

$$\text{or Log}_e T_{max} - \text{Log}_e T_{min} = \mu\alpha$$

In terms of logs to the base 10 this equation is

$$\text{Log}_{10} T_{max} - \text{Log}_{10} T_{min} = 0.4343\mu\alpha$$

5. Problem

As an example, suppose we were to lower a patient in a wheelchair down a 30 degree ramp. The total weight of patient and wheelchair is 200 lb. A rope tied to the wheelchair takes a half turn around a pipe at the top of the ramp,

the coefficient of friction between the rope and the pipe being 0.2.

QUESTION: What force must be applied to the rope to control the motion of the chair and patient?

SOLUTION: From a free body diagram of the wheelchair we find the force in the rope to be 100 lb. Since the rope takes a half turn around the pipe, α is π radians. Substituting in the basic equations,

$$\text{Log}_{10} T_{max} - \text{Log}_{10} T_{min} = 0.4343\mu\alpha$$
$$\text{Log}_{10} 100 - \text{Log}_{10} T_{min} = 0.4343 \times 0.2 \times \pi$$
$$\text{Log}_{10} T_{min} = \text{Log}_{10} 100 - 0.4343 \times 0.2 \times \pi$$
$$\text{Log}_{10} T_{min} = 2 - 0.2726 = 1.7274$$

Looking up the mantissa 0.7274 in the log table gives 534, and the characteristic of 1 indicates that two digits are to appear to the left of the decimal point so,

$$T_{min} = 53.4 \text{ lb.}$$

Friction within the Body. Friction within the body exists between joint surfaces, between layers of tissues, and around structures which slide on one another. Indeed, frictional effects are present down to the microscopic level in the complex body systems.

Sacs filled with fluid are frequently located at sites of wear. These are called bursae and are found between layers of muscle tissue and tendon, between connective tissue structures, such as fascia, fat, and bone, and beneath skin that moves across bony prominences, such as the olecranon. Bursae are flattened structures with smooth mucosal linings, and they serve to decrease friction occurring between moving surfaces. Important examples are the large subacromial bursa, which allows the humeral head to slip underneath the acromial process when the arm is elevated, the trochanteric bursa beneath the abductor tendons at the hip, and bursae around the patellar ligament and tendon of Achilles insertion. A bursa may develop at a site subjected to wear where none was present originally.

Tendons passing through bony grooves are supplied with synovial sheaths, which reduce friction and wear. The long head of the biceps brachii, and the flexor and extensor tendons at the wrist and ankle are examples. Relationships between forces in the tendon and the friction between the tendon and its sheath where it passes around a bony prominence may be investigated by the same method used in the preceding problem.

6. Problem

Suppose we are attempting to find the coefficient of friction existing between the peroneus longus tendon and its sheath as it passes around the lateral malleolus.

QUESTION: Find the value of μ.

SOLUTION: By measurement we might find that T_{max} is 75.0 lb. and T_{min} is 74.3 lb. We also note that the direction of the tendon changes as it turns around the malleolus by an angle of 45 degrees (see Fig. 8.10), which is equivalent to $\pi/4$ radians. Substituting in our basic equation,

$$\text{Log}_{10} \, T_{max} - \text{Log}_{10} \, T_{min} - 0.4343\mu\alpha$$

$$\text{Log}_{10} \, 75 - \text{Log}_{10} \, 74.3 = 0.4343\mu\frac{\pi}{4}$$

$$\mu = \frac{\text{Log}_{10} \, 75 - \text{Log}_{10} \, 74.3}{0.4343\frac{\pi}{4}}$$

$$\mu = \frac{1.8751 - 1.8710}{0.4343\frac{\pi}{4}}$$

$$\mu = 0.012$$

The articular surfaces of the joints glide and pivot during movement and, as we saw earlier, sustain tremendous compression forces. Fortunately the coefficient of friction of articular cartilage is extremely low. On the basis of experiments with human knee joint cartilage, Charnley[6] estimated the coefficient of kinetic friction to be about 0.013; others have given a figure of 0.02[7, 8] for normal animal joints. These values are very much lower than the values for engineering materials. This is one of the difficulties in producing an artificial hip prosthesis to substitute for the natural joint. Different types of metal and plastic materials have been used for this purpose with varying degrees of success. A roller bearing design has been suggested as necessary to duplicate the natural low friction mechanism.[8]

The next two problems suggest an approach to calculation of frictional effects in joints of the human body. The coefficient of friction between articular surfaces is assumed to be 0.015, based on experimental tests cited previously.[6, 7, 8] Measurements of the radius of joint curvature were taken from x-ray films.

The problem of determining the effect of the friction force in joints of the body will be developed here by means of an illustration. First it will be necessary to examine the behavior of friction and other forces on an inclined plane. Consider the block resting on a plane making an angle α with the horizontal as shown in Figure 8.11A. The reaction, R, which is the resultant of F and N must be in line with W for equilibrium to exist, and from the geometry of the figure it is apparent that the angle between R and N will be equal to the slope of the inclined plane α. From this we can see that as the slope of the plane increases until the angle of inclination reaches the value of ϕ (the angle of friction), the angle between N and R will also increase to ϕ where F_{max} will be developed (Fig. 8.11B). Now if we attempt to increase the slope of the plane further it will be impossible to increase the angle between R and N since this angle is limited by the coefficient of friction μ. Therefore if the angle were increased R would no longer line up with W, equilibrium could not exist and the block would slide down the plane.

Now we will examine the problem of friction with regard to the curved surface shown in Figure 8.12A. With the applied load centered over the center of curvature, O, the reaction, R,

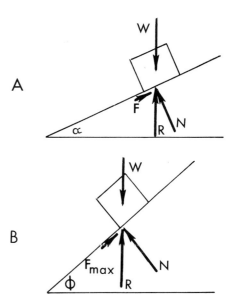

Fig. 8.11. A. Behavior of friction forces on an inclined plane, where α is the angle formed by the plane with the horizontal. N is perpendicular to the plane and W and R are colinear.

B. The slope is increased until the angle of inclination reaches ϕ, the angle of friction.

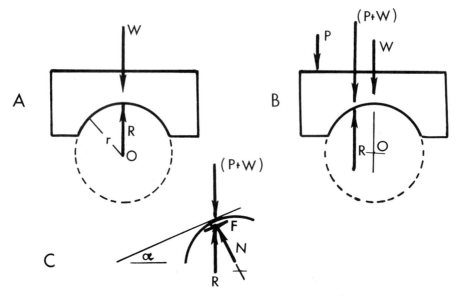

Fig. 8.12. Analysis of friction in relation to a curved surface (see text).

is normal to the surface and no friction exists. If a force, P, is added as shown in Figure 8.12*B*, the resultant of the applied load moves to the left as shown, and for equilibrium to exist the re-action, R, must also move to the left to coincide with it. This reaction is the resultant of a normal force which passes through the center of cur-vature and a frictional force which is tangent to the curve at the point of load application. As shown in Figure 8.12*C*, this is analogous to the inclined plane problem just described. As the resultant moves farther from the center of cur-vature, the slope of the plane increases and the angle between R and N will increase until the angle of φ (the angle of friction) is reached. With further movement of the resultant, equilib-rium will be destroyed and motion will occur. Two problems will be used to illustrate these principles.

7. Problem

Consider the tibio-talar joint with the weight of the body of a 200 lb. man centered over the center of curvature of the talus surface (Fig. 8.13*A*). Then a 100 lb. force will be acting on each ankle (neglecting the weight of the foot) and all muscle forces will be zero.

QUESTION: What force must be exerted through the Achilles tendon by the leg muscles before the joint starts to move?

SOLUTION: With the addition of a force, T (Fig. 8.13*B*), in the tendon acting at a distance

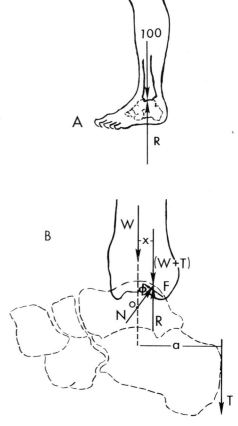

Fig. 8.13. Calculation of friction at the tibio-talar joint (see text).

'a' from the vertical axis through the center of curvature, the first step is to find the distance 'x' to the resultant of W and T. Taking moments about W

$$Ta = x(W + T) \quad or \quad x = \frac{Ta}{W + T}$$

With motion impending, the angle between N and R (and between N and the vertical also) will be the angle of friction ϕ. We have previously determined the relationship between the coefficient of friction and ϕ to be

$$\mu = \tan \phi$$

From the figure

$$Sin \phi = \frac{x}{r}$$

where r is the radius of curvature, and for small angles, such as occur in joint friction, the sine of the angle is approximately equal to the tangent. Then we can write

$$\sin \phi \approx \tan \phi = \mu = \frac{x}{r}$$

Substituting the previously obtained expression for x we have

$$\mu = \frac{Ta}{r(W + T)}$$

and solving this for the maximum value of T which can be developed before motion occurs we obtain

$$T = \frac{\mu r W}{a - \mu r}$$

If we assume the coefficient of friction to be 0.015, and measure r and a and obtain 1.1 and 2.5 in. respectively, we can substitute these values in this equation and solve for T:

$$T = \frac{0.015 \times 1.1 \times 100}{2.5 - 0.015 \times 1.1}$$

$$T = 0.66 \text{ lb.}$$

8. Problem

A previous problem (Fig. 5.43, p. 60) required the determination of the necessary force of elbow flexion to balance a load applied to the horizontal forearm. In this solution friction was ignored and the muscle and joint forces were determined to be 187 and 158 lb. respectively.

QUESTION: If the coefficient of friction in the elbow joint is 0.015, what change in the pre-

viously determined value of muscle force will be required (a) to raise the load, and (b) to just support it? The measured value of the radius of curvature of the joint is 0.75 in.

SOLUTION: Since the joint force was previously determined to be 158 lb. the resultant R of the muscle force and applied load must be equal, opposite and colinear with it through the center of curvature of the joint. (Here we will simplify the problem by ignoring the humero-radial friction and allowing T to represent the flexor muscle group.) Now if the force in the muscle is increased by an amount T, the resultant of J and T will move to the right as shown in Figure 8.14. Solving for the position of this resultant

$$2T = X(J + T)$$
$$x = \frac{2T}{J + T}$$

we can also write

$$\sin \phi \approx \tan \phi = \mu = \frac{x}{r}$$

Combining these equations

$$\mu = \frac{2T}{r(J + T)}$$

and

$$T = \frac{\mu r J}{2 - \mu r}$$

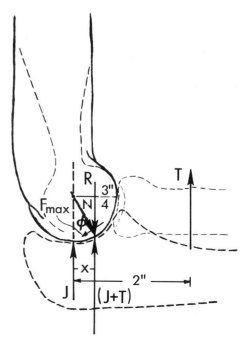

Fig. 8.14. Calculation of friction between the humerus and ulna (see text).

Substituting the given values in this equation

$$T = \frac{0.015 \times 0.75 \times 158}{2 - 0.015 \times 0.75}$$
$$T = 1.19 \text{ lb.}$$

Therefore the muscle force required to just begin to lift the load will be 187 + 1.19 or 188.19 lb. and the minimum muscle force necessary to support the load will be 187 − 1.19 or 185.81 lb., providing the static coefficient of friction is 0.015.

It appears from our calculations that frictional effects at the joints are small in relation to articular compression forces. However, if the coefficient of friction were increased under pathological conditions, these relationships would change.

The role of synovial fluid in joint lubrication is under investigation. The accepted theory has been that synovial fluid is necessary for proper function of joints and has special viscous properties due to a complex mucopolysaccharide it contains—hyaluronic acid. A fluid film between the joint surfaces is believed to absorb the frictional effects of motion and protect the articular cartilage from wear. Lack of fluid in a "dry joint" has been observed clinically to cause pain and to hinder normal function. On the other hand, some investigators contend that the synovial fluid in a joint has little or no importance to movement. When tested in an artificial joint, synovial fluid was found by Ropes et al.[9] to have questionable lubricating properties. It has been claimed that after synovial fluid was wiped from the articular surfaces of joints, the coefficient of friction was not significantly altered.[6] The concept of a "synovial sponge" has been advanced in which synovial fluid is believed to be extruded from the cartilaginous surfaces as the articular cartilage is compressed. "It thus becomes impossible to decide whether the smear of synovial fluid which may be present on the joint surfaces derives from the joint cavity and is laid on the sliding surfaces, or whether the sliding surfaces generate the synovial fluid."[7] If the latter is the case, synovial fluid can be considered merely a by-product of function.

Friction in the joints is of help in stabilizing the body when one is standing still. Since the synovial fluid is believed to be squeezed out from between the articular surfaces when they are under load for some time, the frictional force in the joint, which always acts to oppose motion, acts to hold the body in equilibrium. The frictional forces are, of course, augmented by muscle and ligamentous forces to maintain balance, but balance is not provided by these structures alone. Another factor in joint stability is the deformation of the articular cartilages as they are placed under load.

The many divergent views regarding joint function indicate that a great deal more experimental work must be done before normal and pathologic articular mechanisms are well understood. Indeed, this can be said also of the many areas of biomechanics as the subject is applied to muscoloskeletal function of the human body and to the useful application of this knowledge in patient care.

Bibliography

1. Knocke, F. J., and Knocke, L. S.: *Orthopaedic Nursing.* Philadelphia, F. A. Davis Co., 1945, p. 366.
2. *Ibid,* p. 365.
3. Jackson, Ruth: *The Cervical Syndrome.* 2nd ed., Springfield, Ill., Charles C Thomas, 1958, p. 148.
4. Judovich, B. D.: Lumbar traction therapy—elimination of physical factors that prevent lumbar stretch. *J. A. M. A., 159*:549–50, 1955.
5. Klopsteg, P. E., and Wilson, P. D.: *Human Limbs and their Substitutes.* New York, McGraw-Hill Book Co., Inc., 1954, p. 453.
6. Charnley, J.: The lubrication of animal joints. *Symposium on Biomechanics.* Published by the Institution of Mechanical Engineers, 1 Birdcage Walk, Westminster, London, SW1, 1959, pp. 12–19.
7. Jones, E. D.: Joint lubrication. *Lancet, 1*:1426, 1934.
8. Tanner, R. I.: The lubricating properties of synovial fluid. *Symposium on Biomechanics.* Published by the Institution of Mechanical Engineers, 1 Birdcage Walk, Westminster, London, SW1, 1959, pp. 21–22.
9. Ropes, M. W., Robertson, W. B., Rossmeisl, E. C., Peabody, B., and Bauer, W.: Synovial fluid mucin. *Acta Med. Scand.,* Supplement 196, 1947, pp. 700–734.

Center of Gravity, Segmental Weight and Length Determinations

In much of the literature on locations of centers of gravity of the limbs and trunk, the classic work of Braune and Fischer * has been cited. Recent studies by Dempster † provide more comprehensive data. Excerpts pertinent to the present text are included here through the courtesy of Dr. Dempster, Department of Anatomy, University of Michigan, and the Office of Technical Services, U.S. Department of Commerce. The

* Braune, W. and Fischer, O.: Über den Schwerpunkt des menschlichen Körpers mit Rüchsicht auf die Ausrüstung des deutschen Infanteristem. *Abh. d. K. Sachs Ges. d. Wiss.,* 15, part 2, 1889.

† Dempster, W.: Space Requirements of the Seated Operator. *WADC Technical Report 55-159.,* July, 1955. Report released to the Office of Technical Services, U.S. Dept. of Commerce, Washington 25, D.C.

following sections are based primarily on the report of this work.

Method of Investigation. Eight male cadavers of "more or less medium" build were selected to be dismembered. Seven were embalmed. They ranged in age from 52 to 83 years (two ages unknown). Heights (supine) were 155.3 to 186.6 cm. (61.1 to 73.5 in.) and weights were 109¼ to 159½ lb. After initial anthropometric measurements were made, the hips and shoulders of the cadavers were frozen in a semi-flexed position. This was considered most favorable for apportionment of the tissue to the respective segments on either side of the joint axis. After the limbs were divided from the trunk, the head and trunk segment and the four limb segments were weighed and the center of gravity of each was determined on a balance-plate (segments straight). The limbs were then frozen in a semi-flexed position (elbows 70°; knees 62°) and saw-cuts were made through the joint centers. The resulting eight limb segments were weighed and centers of gravity found. The ankle and wrist joints were frozen in a midposition. The wrist was divided through the head of the capitate bone, at the dorsal wrist crease. The saw-cut through the ankle passed from the upper border of the calcaneus to the tip of the fibular malleolus, just proximal to the head of the talus. Three remaining masses were divided: shoulder girdle, including attaching muscles; head and neck, separated along the upper border of the first rib; and thorax and abdomino-pelvic complex, divided between the last thoracic and first lumbar vertebrae.

After centers of gravity for the parts were determined, distances were measured from these points to the ends of the segments. In order to locate the center of gravity of the various segments in three dimensions, each part was suspended from various points or balanced on the balance-plate. Drill holes were aimed at the center of gravity, dowel sticks inserted in the holes, and saw-cuts made in the plane of the sticks. Specific loci as described by Dempster are shown in Figure 2.11, p. 14.

Surface landmarks associated with joint centers and percentage distance of center of gravity points from joint axes are given in Figure A-1.

Additional observations made by Dempster on living subjects included measurement of strength, range of joint motion, and body dimensions, including limb volume.

Concept of Body Links. In kinematic analysis of human motion, the important moving units are not the various bones, which support the surrounding soft tissue structures, but rather the total mass of the segments which turn about the joint axes. The rotational axes are not located at the junctures of the bones. For example, the axis at the hip lies within the femoral head and at the shoulder, within the humeral head. The humeral head moves downward as the arm is elevated. Both the elbow and knee axes are proximal to the respective articular surfaces. At the radio-carpal and tibio-talar joints, on the other hand, the axis is distal to the joint.

The central straight line, which extends between two axes of rotation, is termed a "link." Thus the femur and humerus are longer than their respective links and the tibia and radius are shorter. The bones form the rigid support required by the segment, but the bone itself is not the link. Link systems are interconnected by joints, which predetermine the particular type of motion permitted to the functional segments. In the case of the hands and feet, the terminal links are considered to extend from the wrist and ankle joint centers to the center of gravity of these so-called "end members."

In apportioning the overlying soft tissue to the respective functional links, some arbitrary decisions must be made. In designating link dimensions, Dempster states: "Such segments are most readily recognized in the limbs, where the segments have a changing angular relation to one another. Skin flexure lines may suggest boundaries in some instances; in others, the establishment of precise boundaries is not easy, since muscles and other structures cross from one region to the next, so that only the most arbitrary boundary lines can be drawn."* Another difficulty is that the joint axes shift about as the parts move in space. However, the instantaneous centers of motion plotted with the part in various positions are clustered in such a fashion that a mean position of the axis can be designated, which is adequate for our purposes. In certain positions a link may be longer or shorter than the dimension based on a mean center.

In Dempster's view, the most satisfactory division of tissue in the experimental work involving sectioning of the body parts was obtained with the limb joints partially flexed. The following data on dimensions and mass of the

* *Ibid,* p. 69.

functional body components have been obtained and reported with reference to the joint-and-link concept of body movement. Such quantitative data should have great importance for the study of biomechanics.

Body and Link Dimensions. Table A-1 gives Dempster's estimates of link dimensions on living subjects (adult men). These represent the distances between joint centers at either end of the links, or between the joint center and center of gravity in the case of the hand and foot. In Table A-2 relative length relationships between

TABLE A-1.   Estimates of Link Dimensions*†

SEGMENT	50TH PERCENTILE	LINK-TO-LENGTH RATIO (PER CENT)	5TH AND 95TH PERCENTILES	
Humerus link	11.9	89.0	11.3	12.6
Humerus length	13.3		12.6	14.1
Radius link	10.7	107.0	10.1	11.2
Radius length	10.0		9.4	10.5
Hand link (wrist center to center of gravity)	2.8	20.6	2.6	2.9
Hand length	7.5		6.9	8.0
Femur link	17.1	91.4	15.9	18.1
Femur length	18.7		17.4	19.8
Tibial link	16.1	110.0	15.0	17.3
Tibial length	14.6		13.6	15.7
Foot link (talus center point to center of gravity)	3.2	30.6	3.0	3.5
Foot length	10.5		9.8	11.3
Vertical distance from mid-talus to floor level	3.2			

* Dempster, W.: Space Requirements of the Seated Operator. *WADC Technical Report 55–159,* July, 1955. Report released to the Office of Technical Services, U.S. Dept. of Commerce, Washington 25, D.C.

† Young adult men, based on ratios from cadaver measurements (inches).

TABLE A-2.   Relative Dimensions of Limb Links*†

	ARM	FOREARM	HAND‡	THIGH	LEG	FOOT‡
Arm		10:9 111%	13:3 432%	7:10 69%	3:4 74%	8:3 369%
Forearm	9:10 90%		4:1 388%	5:8 62%	2:3 66%	10:3 332%
Hand‡	3:13 23%	1:4 26%		1:6 16%	1:6 17%	6:7 85%
Thigh	10:7 144%	8:5 161%	6:1 625%		16:15 107%	16:3 533%
Leg	4:3 135%	3:2 150%	6:1 585%	15:16 94%		5:1 500%
Foot‡	3:8 27%	3:10 30%	7:6 117%	3:16 19%	1:5 20%	

* Dempster, W.: Space Requirements of the Seated Operator. *WADC Technical Report 55–159,* July, 1955. Report released to the Office of Technical Services, U.S. Dept. of Commerce, Washington 25, D.C.

† Proportion and percentage relationships of segments listed in column at left to segments in row across top of chart.

‡ Hand and foot links terminate in centers of gravity of the segments.

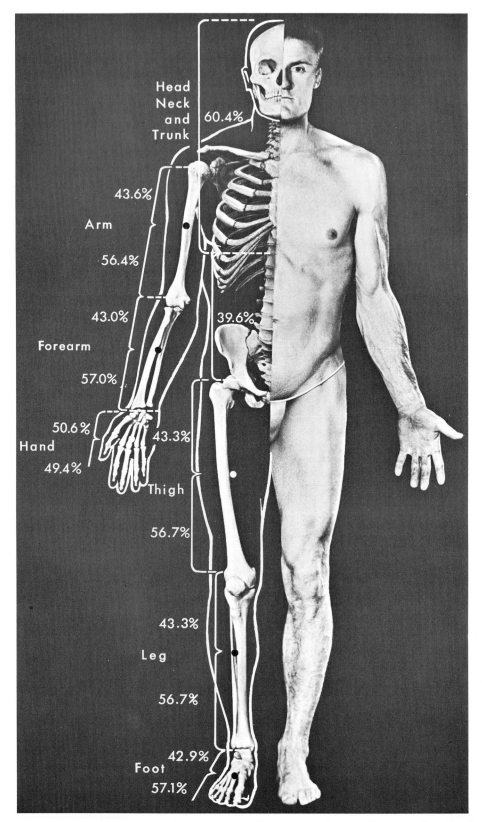

Fig. A-1. Link boundaries (at the joint centers) and percentage distance of centers of gravity from link boundaries. (Figures from Dempster.) (See opposite page.)

SURFACE LANDMARKS ASSOCIATED WITH JOINT CENTERS

Glenohumeral.

Mid-region of palpable bony mass of head and tuberosities of humerus.

Elbow.

Mid-point of line between: (1) lowest palpable point of medial epicondyle of humerus, and (2) a point 8 mm. above radio-humeral junction.

Wrist.

(Palmar surface) Distal skin crease at palmaris longus tendon; or mid-point of line between radial styloid and center of pisiform bone.

(Dorsal surface) Palpable groove between lunate and capitate bones, on a line with metacarpal III.

Hip.

(Lateral aspect) Tip of femoral trochanter 0.4 in. anterior to most laterally projecting part of femoral trochanter.

Knee.

Midpoint of line between centers of posterior convexities of femoral condyles.

Ankle.

At level of line between tip of lateral malleolus of fibula and a point 5 mm distal to tibial malleolus.

LINK LENGTHS are distances between the respective joint centers.

Hand link: slightly oblique line from wrist joint center to center of gravity of the hand.

Foot link: line between ankle joint center and center of gravity of the foot.

the various limb segments are given. Thigh and leg, arm and forearm, and foot and hand links are nearly equal to each other. Another useful comparison among segments is the remarkably constant location of the center of gravity of the arm, forearm, thigh, and leg when considered in terms of percentage distance from the proximal to distal axes of rotation. Deviations of loci in these segments were found to be less than 1 per cent (Fig. A-1). Centers of gravity of the limb segments lie along link lines (lines connecting adjacent joint axes).

On the basis of the various anthropometric measurements, joint range and link dimensions, a drafting board manikin of a seated male figure was developed by Dempster's group for use in cockpit design. Three sizes were suggested, based on large, medium, and small body build. The pattern for a figure of average dimensions has been adapted for use in this text (Fig. A-2). Such a model should be helpful in diagramming and solving problems, as was mentioned in Chapter 5, p. 51.

Dempster's report does not include percentage ratios of link or bone length to total body height. However, Trotter and Gleser's * data are cited, based on measurements of 710 white Army men,

* Trotter, M., and Gleser, G. C.: Estimation of stature from long bones of American whites and negroes. *Am. J. Phys. Anthrop.,* 10:463–514, 1952.

Scale $\frac{1}{4}'' = 1\frac{1}{2}''$

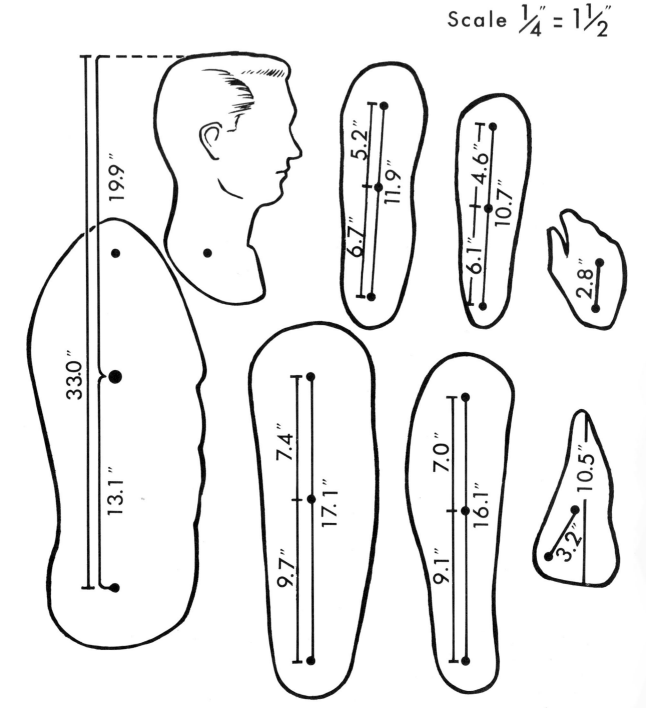

Fig. A-2. Pattern for manikin. Dimensions are adapted from Dempster's drawing board model for a man of average build (*op. cit.,* pp. 124, 155). Segment lengths are based on a total height of about 5 feet, 9½ inches, with proportionate percentage distances in inches between joint axes and centers of gravity (scale ¼ inch = 1½ inch). Anterior aspect of segments is to right (except hand and foot). The outline may be transferred to cardboard, cut out and assembled at axis points by paper fasteners. The figure may then be positioned on ¼ inch graph paper and a tracing made. (Holes through centers of gravity will allow marking of these points.) A suitable scale for segment weights is ¼ inch (one square) = either 2 or 5 pounds, depending on the problem. One may prefer to fit tracing paper over the pattern segments and to draw a figure by matching up the joint axes. Positions of the figure should be as realistic as possible. The many shapes of the spine in various trunk postures, and the wide range of shoulder motion require adjustment of the outline.

TABLE A-3. Mass of the Body Parts*†

			AXIAL SKELETON				
	BODY WEIGHT		Trunk minus limbs	Per cent	Head and neck	Per cent	
Mean	131.5	Mean	74.0	56.5	10.1	7.9	
Range	109.7–159.5	Range	64.5–89.2	52.2–61.1	8.3–11.7	6.5–8.9	

UPPER LIMB

	Entire Limb				Arm			
	Mean	*Per cent*	*Range*	*Per cent*	*Mean*	*Per cent*	*Range*	*Per cent*
Mean	6.4	4.9	4.7–8.7	4.3–5.6	3.5	2.7	2.5–4.8	2.4–3.3
Range	6.3	4.8	4.7–8.6	4.3–5.4	3.4	2.6	2.5–4.8	2.3–3.0

	Forearm and Hand				Forearm			
	Mean	*Per cent*	*Range*	*Per cent*	*Mean*	*Per cent*	*Range*	*Per cent*
Right	2.9	2.2	2.2–3.9	1.8–2.6	2.1	1.6	1.6–2.8	1.3–1.8
Left	2.8	2.1	2.2–3.7	1.8–2.5	2.0	1.5	1.5–2.6	1.3–1.7

	Hand			
	Mean	*Per cent*	*Range*	*Per cent*
Right	.85	0.6	.65–1.1	0.5–0.9
Left	.83	0.6	.70–1.1	0.6–0.9

LOWER LIMB

	Entire Limb				Thigh			
	Mean	*Per cent*	*Range*	*Per cent*	*Mean*	*Per cent*	*Range*	*Per cent*
Right	20.9	15.7	13.6–26.2	12.0–19.5	12.7	9.6	7.4–15.7	6.6–11.9
Left	20.7	15.7	13.7–22.2	12.1–18.8	12.8	9.7	7.7–16.9	6.8–12.7

	Leg and Foot				Leg			
	Mean	*Per cent*	*Range*	*Per cent*	*Mean*	*Per cent*	*Range*	*Per cent*
Right	7.9	5.9	5.7–10.6	5.1–6.7	6.0	4.5	4.3–8.6	3.7–5.4
Left	7.7	6.0	5.7–10.6	5.1–6.7	6.0	4.5	4.3–8.5	3.8–5.3

	Foot			
	Mean	*Per cent*	*Range*	*Per cent*
Right	1.9	1.4	1.4–2.4	1.3–1.5
Left	1.9	1.4	1.6–2.7	1.3–1.7

* Dempster, W.: Space Requirements of the Seated Operator. *WADC Technical Report 55-159*, July, 1955. Report released to the Office of Technical Services, U.S. Dept. of Commerce, Washington 25, D.C.

† Weights in pounds and ratios of parts to total body weight (eight male subjects from middle to old age).

in which the lengths of certain bones are plotted against stature. Extrapolating from these charts we find that at the mid-range of the distribution for the 50th percentile group (average height, 68.9 in., or 1750 mm.) ratios were approximately as follows:

Ratio of stature to length of

femur	1750:477mm.	(27.3%)	18.8 in. (bone length)
tibia	1750:372mm.	(21.2%)	14.6 in. (bone length)
humerus	1750:338mm.	(19.3%)	13.3 in. (bone length)
radius	1750:252mm.	(14.4%)	9.9 in. (bone length)

These figures, together with the data in Table A-1, will be helpful in estimating segment and link lengths in setting up problems. Such estimates, which can be made on oneself, on another person, or from photographs and moving pictures, are admittedly rough approximations but can be of great practical value if careful attention is paid to anatomical landmarks.

Mass of the Body Parts. Basic material on segment weights from Dempster's study was given in Chapter 2 (Fig. 2.11, p. 14). Additional data are presented in Table A-3.

Summary of Braune and Fischer's Data

These data are based on measurements of three cadavers. The limb segments were divided at the joint axes. Total heights of the cadavers were 66.9 in., 66.5 in., and 65.8 in.; mean height was 66.1 in. Weights were 165.6 lb., 122.8 lb., and 133.9 lb. respectively; mean weight was 140.8 lb. Landmarks were defined as follows:

1. *Upper limb.* Steel pins were inserted through the humeral head in the anteroposterior direction and through the head of the capitate bone. The elbow axis was marked medially and laterally on the skin.

2. *Lower limb.* The skin was marked over the anterior superior iliac spine, upper prominence of the greater trochanter (considered to be at the level of the center of the femoral head), at the medial and lateral points of the knee axis, and at the medial and lateral points of the ankle axis.

The dimensions of the segments were measured from these landmarks. For center of gravity determinations the cadavers were frozen, segmented, and the parts studied by balancing them over a knife edge and suspending them by slender rods in such a fashion that they were free to oscillate until equilibrium was reached. The head and trunk were included in these investigations.

The figures given below represent the arith-metic means from the three cadavers (right and left limbs combined).

Location of centers of gravity is given in terms of percentage of the distance from proximal to distal joint centers of the segments. (Means of right and left sides of three subjects.)

Additional centers of gravity reported by Braune and Fischer were:

Head: behind the sella turcica in the sagittal plane

Trunk: in or anterior to the first lumbar vertebra

Entire upper limb: in the area of the elbow axis

Entire lower limb: a few centimeters (2 to 5) above the knee axis in the substance of the femur

In the foregoing data, a relatively larger mass was attributed to the limbs as compared with the trunk, in contrast to Dempster's findings. It should be emphasized that all data now available on percentage weights of body parts have been obtained from small samples of subjects, and wide individual variations from these figures must be expected. In a World War II study of body components of 4063 service men made in relation to uniform sizes, not a single man in the group was found to be average in all dimensions.*

* Hertzberg, H. T. E.: Dynamic anthropometry of working positions. Human Factors, 2:147–155, 1960.

SEGMENTAL LENGTH AND WEIGHT

	LENGTH IN INCHES	PER CENT OF TOTAL HEIGHT	WEIGHT IN POUNDS	PER CENT OF TOTAL WEIGHT
Head (chin to apex of skull)	8.2	12.4	9.8	6.9
Trunk			65.2	46.1
Upper limb			8.8	6.3
Arm	12.3	17.2	4.7	3.3
Forearm	10.9	16.5	2.9	2.1
Hand			1.2	0.8
Lower limb			24.1	17.3
Thigh	16.4	24.8	14.9	10.7
Leg	16.5	24.9	6.6	4.7
Foot	10.7	16.3	2.3	1.7

LOCATION OF CENTER OF GRAVITY

	TO PROXIMAL END	TO DISTAL END	
Arm*	.47	.53	On line joining humeral head center and midpoint of elbow axis.
Forearm*	.42	.58	On line joining midpoint of elbow axis and center of capitate bone (hand pronated).
Thigh	.44	.56	On line joining center of femoral head and midpoint of knee axis.
Leg	.42	.58	On line joining midpoint of knee and center of ankle joint.
Foot	.43	.57	

* Mean of two subjects.

Method of Finding the Weight of a Segment

The following is the derivation of the formula suggested on p. 62 for determining the weight of a body part. In Figure A-3 the upper subject lies prone on a board, one end of which rests on a scale. We take moments about the left support:

$$SL = WX$$
$$X = \frac{SL}{W} \tag{1}$$

Then taking moments about the same point, since the moments of the components must be equal to the moment of the resultant,

$$WX = W_1X_1 + W_2X_2 \tag{2}$$

Now applying the same equations to the lower figure,

$$S'L = WX'$$
$$X' = \frac{S'L}{W} \tag{3}$$

and

$$WX' = W_1X_1 + W_2X_2' \tag{4}$$

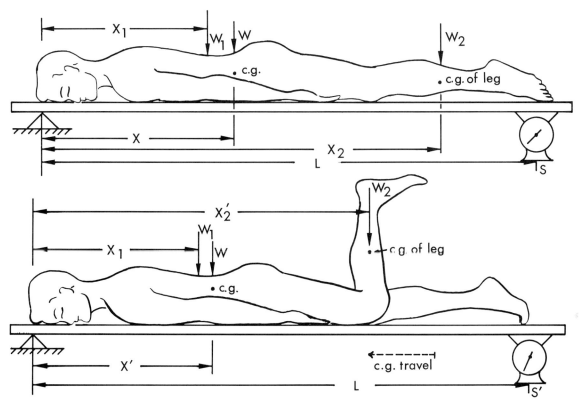

Fig. A-3. Method of finding the weight of a segment of the body.

Subtracting equation (4) from equation (2):

$$WX = W_1X_1 + W_2X_2$$
$$WX' = W_1X_1 + W_2X_2'$$
$$\overline{W(X - X') = W_2(X_2 - X_2')}$$
$$W_2 = \frac{W(X - X')}{(X_2 - X_2')}$$

Substituting equations (1) and (3) for X and X',

$$W_2 = \frac{W\left(\dfrac{SL}{W} - \dfrac{S'L}{W}\right)}{(X_2 - X_2')}$$
$$W_2 = \frac{L(S - S')}{(X_2 - X_2')}$$

Then the weight of the leg and foot, W_2, is equal to the distance between the supports for the board, multiplied by the difference between scale readings with the leg horizontal and with it vertical, and divided by the distance the center of gravity of the leg and foot moves horizontally as the limb moves from the first to the second position.

Mathematical
Tables

These tables are reproduced on the next six pages.

Natural Trigonometric Functions

Degrees	SINES							Cosines
	0′	10′	20′	30′	40′	50′	60′	
0	0.00000	0.00291	0.00582	0.00873	0.01164	0.01454	0.01745	89
1	0.01745	0.02036	0.02327	0.02618	0.02908	0.03199	0.03490	88
2	0.03490	0.03781	0.04071	0.04362	0.04653	0.04943	0.05234	87
3	0.05234	0.05524	0.05814	0.06105	0.06395	0.06685	0.06976	86
4	0.06976	0.07266	0.07556	0.07846	0.08136	0.08426	0.08716	85
5	0.08716	0.09005	0.09295	0.09585	0.09874	0.10164	0.10453	84
6	0.10453	0.10742	0.11031	0.11320	0.11609	0.11898	0.12187	83
7	0.12187	0.12476	0.12764	0.13053	0.13341	0.13629	0.13917	82
8	0.13917	0.14205	0.14493	0.14781	0.15069	0.15356	0.15643	81
9	0.15643	0.15931	0.16218	0.16505	0.16792	0.17078	0.17365	80
10	0.17365	0.17651	0.17937	0.18224	0.18509	0.18795	0.19081	79
11	0.19081	0.19366	0.19652	0.19937	0.20222	0.20507	0.20791	78
12	0.20791	0.21076	0.21360	0.21644	0.21928	0.22212	0.22495	77
13	0.22495	0.22778	0.23062	0.23345	0.23627	0.23910	0.24192	76
14	0.24192	0.24474	0.24756	0.25038	0.25320	0.25601	0.25882	75
15	0.25882	0.26163	0.26443	0.26724	0.27004	0.27284	0.27564	74
16	0.27564	0.27843	0.28123	0.28402	0.28680	0.28959	0.29237	73
17	0.29237	0.29515	0.29793	0.30071	0.30348	0.30625	0.30902	72
18	0.30902	0.31178	0.31454	0.31730	0.32006	0.32282	0.32557	71
19	0.32557	0.32832	0.33106	0.33381	0.33655	0.33929	0.34202	70
20	0.34202	0.34475	0.34748	0.35021	0.35293	0.35565	0.35837	69
21	0.35837	0.36108	0.36379	0.36650	0.36921	0.37191	0.37461	68
22	0.37461	0.37730	0.37999	0.38268	0.38537	0.38805	0.39073	67
23	0.39073	0.39341	0.39608	0.39875	0.40142	0.40408	0.40674	66
24	0.40674	0.40939	0.41204	0.41469	0.41734	0.41998	0.42262	65
25	0.42262	0.42525	0.42788	0.43051	0.43313	0.43575	0.43837	64
26	0.43837	0.44098	0.44359	0.44620	0.44880	0.45140	0.45399	63
27	0.45399	0.45658	0.45917	0.46175	0.46433	0.46690	0.46947	62
28	0.46947	0.47204	0.47460	0.47716	0.47971	0.48226	0.48481	61
29	0.48481	0.48735	0.48989	0.49242	0.49495	0.49748	0.50000	60
30	0.50000	0.50252	0.50503	0.50754	0.51004	0.51254	0.51504	59
31	0.51504	0.51753	0.52002	0.52250	0.52498	0.52745	0.52992	58
32	0.52992	0.53238	0.53484	0.53730	0.53975	0.54220	0.54464	57
33	0.54464	0.54708	0.54951	0.55194	0.55436	0.55678	0.55919	56
34	0.55919	0.56160	0.56401	0.56641	0.56880	0.57119	0.57358	55
35	0.57358	0.57596	0.57833	0.58070	0.58307	0.58543	0.58779	54
36	0.58779	0.59014	0.59248	0.59482	0.59716	0.59949	0.60182	53
37	0.60182	0.60414	0.60645	0.60876	0.61107	0.61337	0.61566	52
38	0.61566	0.61795	0.62024	0.62251	0.62479	0.62706	0.62932	51
39	0.62932	0.63158	0.63383	0.63608	0.63832	0.64056	0.64279	50
40	0.64279	0.64501	0.64723	0.64945	0.65166	0.65386	0.65606	49
41	0.65606	0.65825	0.66044	0.66262	0.66480	0.66697	0.66913	48
42	0.66913	0.67129	0.67344	0.67559	0.67773	0.67987	0.68200	47
43	0.68200	0.68412	0.68624	0.68835	0.69046	0.69256	0.69466	46
44	0.69466	0.69675	0.69883	0.70091	0.70298	0.70505	0.70711	45
Sines	60′	50′	40′	30′	20′	10′	0′	Degrees
	COSINES							

Natural Trigonometric Functions

Degrees	COSINES							Sines
	0′	10′	20′	30′	40′	50′	60′	
0	1.00000	1.00000	0.99998	0.99996	0.99993	0.99989	0.99985	89
1	0.99985	0.99979	0.99973	0.99966	0.99958	0.99949	0.99939	88
2	0.99939	0.99929	0.99917	0.99905	0.99892	0.99878	0.99863	87
3	0.99863	0.99847	0.99831	0.99813	0.99795	0.99776	0.99756	86
4	0.99756	0.99736	0.99714	0.99692	0.99668	0.99644	0.99619	85
5	0.99619	0.99594	0.99567	0.99540	0.99511	0.99482	0.99452	84
6	0.99452	0.99421	0.99390	0.99357	0.99324	0.99290	0.99255	83
7	0.99255	0.99219	0.99182	0.99144	0.99106	0.99067	0.99027	82
8	0.99027	0.98986	0.98944	0.98902	0.98858	0.98814	0.98769	81
9	0.98769	0.98723	0.98676	0.98629	0.98580	0.98531	0.98481	80
10	0.98481	0.98430	0.98378	0.98325	0.98272	0.98218	0.98163	79
11	0.98163	0.98107	0.98050	0.97992	0.97934	0.97875	0.97815	78
12	0.97815	0.97754	0.97692	0.97630	0.97566	0.97502	0.97437	77
13	0.97437	0.97371	0.97304	0.97237	0.97169	0.97100	0.97030	76
14	0.97030	0.96959	0.96887	0.96815	0.96742	0.96667	0.96593	75
15	0.96593	0.96517	0.96440	0.96363	0.96285	0.96206	0.96126	74
16	0.96126	0.96046	0.95964	0.95882	0.95799	0.95715	0.95630	73
17	0.95630	0.95545	0.95459	0.95372	0.95284	0.95195	0.95106	72
18	0.95106	0.95015	0.94924	0.94832	0.94740	0.94646	0.94552	71
19	0.94552	0.94457	0.94361	0.94264	0.94167	0.94068	0.93969	70
20	0.93969	0.93869	0.93769	0.93667	0.93565	0.93462	0.93358	69
21	0.93358	0.93253	0.93148	0.93042	0.92935	0.92827	0.92718	68
22	0.92718	0.92609	0.92499	0.92388	0.92276	0.92164	0.92050	67
23	0.92050	0.91936	0.91822	0.91706	0.91590	0.91472	0.91355	66
24	0.91355	0.91236	0.91116	0.90996	0.90875	0.90753	0.90631	65
25	0.90631	0.90507	0.90383	0.90259	0.90133	0.90007	0.89879	64
26	0.89879	0.89752	0.89623	0.89493	0.89363	0.89232	0.89101	63
27	0.89101	0.88968	0.88835	0.88701	0.88566	0.88431	0.88295	62
28	0.88295	0.88158	0.88020	0.87882	0.87743	0.87603	0.87462	61
29	0.87462	0.87321	0.87178	0.87036	0.86892	0.86748	0.86603	60
30	0.86603	0.86457	0.86310	0.86163	0.86015	0.85866	0.85717	59
31	0.85717	0.85567	0.85416	0.85264	0.85112	0.84959	0.84805	58
32	0.84805	0.84650	0.84495	0.84339	0.84182	0.84025	0.83867	57
33	0.83867	0.83708	0.83549	0.83389	0.83228	0.83066	0.82904	56
34	0.82904	0.82741	0.82577	0.82413	0.82248	0.82082	0.81915	55
35	0.81915	0.81748	0.81580	0.81412	0.81242	0.81072	0.80902	54
36	0.80902	0.80730	0.80558	0.80386	0.80212	0.80038	0.79864	53
37	0.79864	0.79688	0.79512	0.79335	0.79158	0.78980	0.78801	52
38	0.78801	0.78622	0.78442	0.78261	0.78079	0.77897	0.77715	51
39	0.77715	0.77531	0.77347	0.77162	0.76977	0.76791	0.76604	50
40	0.76604	0.76417	0.76229	0.76041	0.75851	0.75661	0.75471	49
41	0.75471	0.75280	0.75088	0.74896	0.74703	0.74509	0.74314	48
42	0.74314	0.74120	0.73924	0.73728	0.73531	0.73333	0.73135	47
43	0.73135	0.72937	0.72737	0.72537	0.72337	0.72136	0.71934	46
44	0.71934	0.71732	0.71529	0.71325	0.71121	0.70916	0.70711	45
Cosines	60′	50′	40′	30′	20′	10′	0′	Degrees
	SINES							

NATURAL TRIGONOMETRIC FUNCTIONS

Degrees	TANGENTS							Cotangents
	0'	10'	20'	30'	40'	50'	60'	
0	0.00000	0.00291	0.00582	0.00873	0.01164	0.01455	0.01746	89
1	0.01746	0.02036	0.02328	0.02619	0.02910	0.03201	0.03492	88
2	0.03492	0.03783	0.04075	0.04366	0.04658	0.04949	0.05241	87
3	0.05241	0.05533	0.05824	0.06116	0.06408	0.06700	0.06993	86
4	0.06993	0.07285	0.07578	0.07870	0.08163	0.08456	0.08749	85
5	0.08749	0.09042	0.09335	0.09629	0.09923	0.10216	0.10510	84
6	0.10510	0.10805	0.11099	0.11394	0.11688	0.11983	0.12278	83
7	0.12278	0.12574	0.12869	0.13165	0.13461	0.13758	0.14054	82
8	0.14054	0.14351	0.14648	0.14945	0.15243	0.15540	0.15838	81
9	0.15838	0.16137	0.16435	0.16734	0.17033	0.17333	0.17633	80
10	0.17633	0.17933	0.18233	0.18534	0.18835	0.19136	0.19438	79
11	0.19438	0.19740	0.20042	0.20345	0.20648	0.20952	0.21256	78
12	0.21256	0.21560	0.21864	0.22169	0.22475	0.22781	0.23087	77
13	0.23087	0.23393	0.23700	0.24008	0.24316	0.24624	0.24933	76
14	0.24933	0.25242	0.25552	0.25862	0.26172	0.26483	0.26795	75
15	0.26795	0.27107	0.27419	0.27732	0.28046	0.28360	0.28675	74
16	0.28675	0.28990	0.29305	0.29621	0.29938	0.30255	0.30573	73
17	0.30573	0.30891	0.31210	0.31530	0.31850	0.32171	0.32492	72
18	0.32492	0.32814	0.33136	0.33460	0.33783	0.34108	0.34433	71
19	0.34433	0.34758	0.35085	0.35412	0.35740	0.36068	0.36397	70
20	0.36397	0.36727	0.37057	0.37388	0.37720	0.38053	0.38386	69
21	0.38386	0.38721	0.39055	0.39391	0.39727	0.40065	0.40403	68
22	0.40403	0.40741	0.41081	0.41421	0.41763	0.42105	0.42447	67
23	0.42447	0.42791	0.43136	0.43481	0.43828	0.44175	0.44523	66
24	0.44523	0.44872	0.45222	0.45573	0.45924	0.46277	0.46631	65
25	0.46631	0.46985	0.47341	0.47698	0.48055	0.48414	0.48773	64
26	0.48773	0.49134	0.49495	0.49858	0.50222	0.50587	0.50953	63
27	0.50953	0.51320	0.51688	0.52057	0.52427	0.52798	0.53171	62
28	0.53171	0.53545	0.53920	0.54296	0.54674	0.55051	0.55431	61
29	0.55431	0.55812	0.56194	0.56577	0.56962	0.57348	0.57735	60
30	0.57735	0.58124	0.58513	0.58905	0.59297	0.59691	0.60086	59
31	0.60086	0.60483	0.60881	0.61280	0.61681	0.62083	0.62487	58
32	0.62487	0.62892	0.63299	0.63707	0.64117	0.64528	0.64941	57
33	0.64941	0.65355	0.65771	0.66189	0.66608	0.67028	0.67451	56
34	0.67451	0.67875	0.68301	0.68728	0.69157	0.69588	0.70021	55
35	0.70021	0.70455	0.70891	0.71329	0.71769	0.72211	0.72654	54
36	0.72654	0.73100	0.73547	0.73996	0.74447	0.74900	0.75355	53
37	0.75355	0.75812	0.76272	0.76733	0.77196	0.77661	0.78129	52
38	0.78129	0.78598	0.79070	0.79544	0.80020	0.80498	0.80978	51
39	0.80978	0.81461	0.81946	0.82434	0.82923	0.83415	0.83910	50
40	0.83910	0.84407	0.84906	0.85408	0.85912	0.86419	0.86929	49
41	0.86929	0.87441	0.87955	0.88473	0.88992	0.89515	0.90040	48
42	0.90040	0.90569	0.91099	0.91633	0.92170	0.92709	0.93252	47
43	0.93252	0.93797	0.94345	0.94896	0.95451	0.96008	0.96569	46
44	0.96569	0.97133	0.97700	0.98270	0.98843	0.99420	1.00000	45
Tangents	60'	50'	40'	30'	20'	10'	0'	Degrees

COTANGENTS

Natural Trigonometric Functions

Degrees	COTANGENTS							Tangents
	0'	10'	20'	30'	40'	50'	60'	
0	∞	343.77371	171.88540	114.58865	85.93979	68.75009	57.28996	89
1	57.28996	49.10388	42.96408	38.18846	34.36777	31.24158	28.63625	88
2	28.63625	26.43160	24.54176	22.90377	21.47040	20.20555	19.08114	87
3	19.08114	18.07498	17.16934	16.34986	15.60478	14.92442	14.30067	86
4	14.30067	13.72674	13.19688	12.70621	12.25051	11.82617	11.43005	85
5	11.43005	11.05943	10.71191	10.38540	10.07803	9.78817	9.51436	84
6	9.51436	9.25530	9.00983	8.77689	8.55555	8.34496	8.14435	83
7	8.14435	7.95302	7.77035	7.59575	7.42871	7.26873	7.11537	82
8	7.11537	6.96823	6.82694	6.69116	6.56055	6.43484	6.31375	81
9	6.31375	6.19703	6.08444	5.97576	5.87080	5.76937	5.67128	80
10	5.67128	5.57638	5.48451	5.39552	5.30928	5.22566	5.14455	79
11	5.14455	5.06584	4.98940	4.91516	4.84300	4.77286	4.70463	78
12	4.70463	4.63825	4.57363	4.51071	4.44942	4.38969	4.33148	77
13	4.33148	4.27471	4.21933	4.16530	4.11256	4.06107	4.01078	76
14	4.01078	3.96165	3.91364	3.86671	3.82083	3.77595	3.73205	75
15	3.73205	3.68909	3.64705	3.60588	3.56557	3.52609	3.48741	74
16	3.48741	3.44951	3.41236	3.37594	3.34023	3.30521	3.27085	73
17	3.27085	3.23714	3.20406	3.17159	3.13972	3.10842	3.07768	72
18	3.07768	3.04749	3.01783	2.98869	2.96004	2.93189	2.90421	71
19	2.90421	2.87700	2.85023	2.82391	2.79802	2.77254	2.74748	70
20	2.74748	2.72281	2.69853	2.67462	2.65109	2.62791	2.60509	69
21	2.60509	2.58261	2.56046	2.53865	2.51715	2.49597	2.47509	68
22	2.47509	2.45451	2.43422	2.41421	2.39449	2.37504	2.35585	67
23	2.35585	2.33693	2.31826	2.29984	2.28167	2.26374	2.24604	66
24	2.24604	2.22857	2.21132	2.19430	2.17749	2.16090	2.14451	65
25	2.14451	2.12832	2.11233	2.09654	2.08094	2.06553	2.05030	64
26	2.05030	2.03526	2.02039	2.00569	1.99116	1.97680	1.96261	63
27	1.96261	1.94858	1.93470	1.92098	1.90741	1.89400	1.88073	62
28	1.88073	1.86760	1.85462	1.84177	1.82907	1.81649	1.80405	61
29	1.80405	1.79174	1.77955	1.76749	1.75556	1.74375	1.73205	60
30	1.73205	1.72047	1.70901	1.69766	1.68643	1.67530	1.66428	59
31	1.66428	1.65337	1.64256	1.63185	1.62125	1.61074	1.60033	58
32	1.60033	1.59002	1.57981	1.56969	1.55966	1.54972	1.53987	57
33	1.53987	1.53010	1.52043	1.51084	1.50133	1.49190	1.48256	56
34	1.48256	1.47330	1.46411	1.45501	1.44598	1.43703	1.42815	55
35	1.42815	1.41934	1.41061	1.40195	1.39336	1.38484	1.37638	54
36	1.37638	1.36800	1.35968	1.35142	1.34323	1.33511	1.32704	53
37	1.32704	1.31904	1.31110	1.30323	1.29541	1.28764	1.27994	52
38	1.27994	1.27230	1.26471	1.25717	1.24969	1.24227	1.23490	51
39	1.23490	1.22758	1.22031	1.21310	1.20593	1.19882	1.19175	50
40	1.19175	1.18474	1.17777	1.17085	1.16398	1.15715	1.15037	49
41	1.15037	1.14363	1.13694	1.13029	1.12369	1.11713	1.11061	48
42	1.11061	1.10414	1.09770	1.09131	1.08496	1.07864	1.07237	47
43	1.07237	1.06613	1.05994	1.05378	1.04766	1.04158	1.03553	46
44	1.03553	1.02952	1.02355	1.01761	1.01170	1.00583	1.00000	45

Cotangents	60'	50'	40'	30'	20'	10'	0'	Degrees
	TANGENTS							

Common Logarithms

N.	0	1	2	3	4	5	6	7	8	9
10	0000	0043	0086	0128	0170	0212	0253	0294	0334	0374
11	0414	0453	0492	0531	0569	0607	0645	0682	0719	0755
12	0792	0828	0864	0899	0934	0969	1004	1038	1072	1106
13	1139	1173	1206	1239	1271	1303	1335	1367	1399	1430
14	1461	1492	1523	1553	1584	1614	1644	1673	1703	1732
15	1761	1790	1818	1847	1875	1903	1931	1959	1987	2014
16	2041	2068	2095	2122	2148	2175	2201	2227	2253	2279
17	2304	2330	2355	2380	2405	2430	2455	2480	2504	2529
18	2553	2577	2601	2625	2648	2672	2695	2718	2742	2765
19	2788	2810	2833	2856	2878	2900	2923	2945	2967	2989
20	3010	3032	3054	3075	3096	3118	3139	3160	3181	3201
21	3222	3243	3263	3284	3304	3324	3345	3365	3385	3404
22	3424	3444	3464	3483	3502	3522	3541	3560	3579	3598
23	3617	3636	3655	3674	3692	3711	3729	3747	3766	3784
24	3802	3820	3838	3856	3874	3892	3909	3927	3945	3962
25	3979	3997	4014	4031	4048	4065	4082	4099	4116	4133
26	4150	4166	4183	4200	4216	4232	4249	4265	4281	4298
27	4314	4330	4346	4362	4378	4393	4409	4425	4440	4456
28	4472	4487	4502	4518	4533	4548	4564	4579	4594	4609
29	4624	4639	4654	4669	4683	4698	4713	4728	4742	4757
30	4771	4786	4800	4814	4829	4843	4857	4871	4886	4900
31	4914	4928	4942	4955	4969	4983	4997	5011	5024	5038
32	5051	5065	5079	5092	5105	5119	5132	5145	5159	5172
33	5185	5198	5211	5224	5237	5250	5263	5276	5289	5302
34	5315	5328	5340	5353	5366	5378	5391	5403	5416	5428
35	5441	5453	5465	5478	5490	5502	5514	5527	5539	5551
36	5563	5575	5587	5599	5611	5623	5635	5647	5658	5670
37	5682	5694	5705	5717	5729	5740	5752	5763	5775	5786
38	5798	5809	5821	5832	5843	5855	5866	5877	5888	5899
39	5911	5922	5933	5944	5955	5966	5977	5988	5999	6010
40	6021	6031	6042	6053	6064	6075	6085	6096	6107	6117
41	6128	6138	6149	6160	6170	6180	6191	6201	6212	6222
42	6232	6243	6253	6263	6274	6284	6294	6304	6314	6325
43	6335	6345	6355	6365	6375	6385	6395	6405	6415	6425
44	6435	6444	6454	6464	6474	6484	6493	6503	6513	6522
45	6532	6542	6551	6561	6571	6580	6590	6599	6609	6618
46	6628	6637	6646	6656	6665	6675	6684	6693	6702	6712
47	6721	6730	6739	6749	6758	6767	6776	6785	6794	6803
48	6812	6821	6830	6839	6848	6857	6866	6875	6884	6893
49	6902	6911	6920	6928	6937	6946	6955	6964	6972	6981
50	6990	6998	7007	7016	7024	7033	7042	7050	7059	7067
51	7076	7084	7093	7101	7110	7118	7126	7135	7143	7152
52	7160	7168	7177	7185	7193	7202	7210	7218	7226	7235
53	7243	7251	7259	7267	7275	7284	7292	7300	7308	7316
54	7324	7332	7340	7348	7356	7364	7372	7380	7388	7396
N.	0	1	2	3	4	5	6	7	8	9

Kinematics.   Study of relation between displacement, velocity and acceleration.

Kinetics.   Study of moving bodies including forces producing motion.

Line diagram.   Simple graphic portrayal of body or part.

Link.   Distance between joint centers of body segments.

Mass.   Weight divided by acceleration of gravity $\left(\dfrac{W}{g}\right)$ units $\dfrac{\text{lb. sec.}^2}{\text{ft.}}$

Mechanics.   Study of the action of forces on bodies.

Moment of force.   Product of force and distance (moment arm) from any point to action line of force.

Momentum.   Product of mass and its velocity.

Normal.   Perpendicular to surface.

Parallelogram law.   The resultant of two concurrent forces is the diagonal of a parallelogram whose sides are the original forces.

Polygon.   Multi-sided figure.

Power.   Time rate of doing work, e.g., ft.-lb. per minute.

Resultant.   Simplest equivalent force system which will replace any given system.

Rotary (rotatory) motion.   Rotation; motion in which all points describe circular arcs about a line or axis.

Rectangular components.   Components of a force at right angles to each other.

Rectilinear motion.   Motion in which all points in a body describe straight parallel lines.

Scalar quantity.   Quantity having magnitude only.

Statics.   Study of forces acting on bodies at rest.

Strain.   Deformation (lengthening or shortening) of any body or member.

Stress.   Internal force between molecules.

Torque.   Moment of force (term generally applied to rotation of shafts).

Translatory motion.   Motion in which all points in a body describe parallel lines, either straight or curved.

Triangle law. $R = \sqrt{P^2 + Q^2 + 2\,PQ\cos\theta}$.

Vector quantity.   Quantity having both magnitude and direction.

Velocity.   Time rate of change of displacement.

Work.   Product of force and displacement.